Sara Yeomans was born ... grew up there. In 1961 sh... students to go to Susse... English and gained a deg...

She has also studied theatre direction and has worked as a teacher, a scriptwriter and director, a freelance writer and journalist, and as assistant editor on the magazine *Devon Life*.

Sara Yeomans has three daughters and lives and works in Devon.

Travels with a Pram
AND
Hot Flush AND THE Toy Boy
SARA YEOMANS

First published by The Women's Press Ltd, 1994
A member of the Namara Group
34 Great Sutton Street, London EC1V 0DX

British Library Cataloguing-in-Publication Data
    Yeomans, Sara
    Travels with a Pram and Hot Flush and the Toy Boy
    I. Title
    823 [F]

ISBN 0 7043 4338 X

Typeset in Bembo by Contour Typesetters, Southall, London
Printed and bound in Great Britain

To Polly, Topsy and Chloë, with lots of love

Acknowledgements

I would like to thank everybody who let me make sausages, drive buses, row boats, catch salmon, record songs, and watch a rehearsal of *Top of the Pops*.

I must also thank *She* magazine for allowing me to reprint some of the material which was originally published by them.

Chapter 1

I drew out the Family Allowance and looked at my shopping list. Potatoes, loo paper, toothpaste, nappy steriliser ... It suddenly seemed a terrible waste of life and money to spend the sweet FA on the boring old things I always spent it on. I felt sin welling up inside me. It was wonderful. So I looked around for something good and dutiful to lead me out of temptation and back to the sink. Parked across the road was a bus with 'Races' written across its front.

'Sorry lady,' said the driver as I wheeled Sophie up to the door. 'No prams.'

I was about to back down and plod home to virtue when a sharp voice squawked from the back of the bus: 'Why not?'

The driver turned round. 'I can't be expected to heave babies and prams up and down these steps all day.'

'Come on Doris, give us a hand.' Two fat old women with hats and walking sticks waddled down the aisle. They hung their sticks over the ticket machine and grinned at me. 'You take the baby, love, and we'll see to the pram.'

They hauled and squeezed it up the steps and plonked it in the gangway. 'It's an obstruction,' whined the driver.

'Miserable bugger,' said the fatter old woman, 'cheer up or we'll hijack you.'

They unhooked their walking sticks. 'Drive on, my

man,' said the one called Doris, grandly. And much to my surprise, he did.

When we got to the racecourse, Doris and her friend unloaded us and staggered off to find a bookie. Sophie and the pram and I arrived at the turnstile. We couldn't get through, but the turnstile man was more imaginative than the bus driver. 'Go round to the left, lady,' he said cheerfully, 'you can get through the horses' gate.' So Sophie and I made a stately entrance in the middle of a line of rich, smooth racehorses, and ended up at the Owners' Paddock.

I am not one of those women who chooses a horse because of its pretty name or because the jockey's colours match her nightie. I do it properly. I bought a race card and studied the form. I narrowed my eyes and screwed up my face professionally as a batch of ten horses circled the paddock. I chose a bouncy bay called Space Hopper who had been placed in his last three races. I reckoned he was due for a win.

Then I found a bookie called Harry Spree who had a kind face and who was offering twelve to one on my horse. 'Pound each way on Space Hopper,' I said as if I backed horses every day of my life instead of just once a year on the Grand National. I handed over two pounds and found a good viewing space. Needless to say, Space Hopper bounded into the lead and fell over his feet at the first fence. Two pounds down and three pounds and eighty-five pence to go. My next choice was a blinkered grey called Milk Shake who went backwards under starter's orders and then settled down into last place for the whole of his race. Four pounds gone. As I looked sadly at the horses parading the paddock before the last race, I realised that I'd only got one pound and eighty-five pence and my bus fare left for the rest of the week and there was nothing for Roger's tea. A funny-looking black horse meandered past me and I glanced at his name on the card. Teapot. One pound and eighty-five pence wasn't going to be much use whichever way you looked at it, so I took fifteen pence out of the bus fare and handed two pounds over to Harry Spree, who was offering a hundred to one on Teapot.

They were under starter's orders, all seven of them, and then they were off. Teapot left in fifth place and lumbered up to the first fence. Then he stuck his nose in the air, arched his tail, flew into a tremendous leap that overtook two horses in mid-air and landed in third place. My heart began to beat faster. 'Come on, Teapot!' I shrieked as he loped past us. 'You're a beautiful Teapot! You're a wonderful horse!'

I swear he heard me. He raised one eyebrow and put on a spurt. Over the next three fences he moved into second place behind a powerful animal called Mullarkey, the favourite. They were miles out on the other side of the course now. The commentator shrieked 'And it's Mullarkey the favourite two lengths ahead of Teapot the outsider . . .'

'Keep going, Teapot,' I prayed. 'Good boy, Teapot, I love you, old horse.' They swung round the bend and into view.

'Teapot! Teapot!' I yelled, while all around me lungs were emptying for Mullarkey. As the runners approached the final jump I stuck my nose in the air and howled my horse's name. He bunched up and flung himself over the fence, leaving Mullarkey a nose behind. I bounced the pram in time with hoofs, chanting and jumping and embarrassing Sophie, who looked the other way and tried to pretend that I was nothing to do with her. Teapot crossed the line half a length ahead of Mullarkey, I burst into tears and Harry Spree turned pale.

I bought cans of lager and a bottle of champagne for everyone on the bus (except the driver) and we arrived back in town in a disgusting state just before the shops shut. I swayed off the bus clutching Sophie and reeled into the butcher's. 'Pig's liver?' asked Duncan our butcher when he saw me, 'or is it mince today?'

'Two steaks, please,' I replied with dignity and then remembered I'd left the pram on the bus. I thrust Sophie into Duncan's arms and rushed back to the bus stop. The bus had gone, but Doris and her friend had rescued us again. The pram was parked in the shelter with a heap of empty lager cans inside it. I went back to collect Sophie and the steaks, bought a bottle of red wine at the Co-op, and floated home to prepare supper.

'Have you come into a fortune or something?' asked Roger when he saw the steak and wine.

I looked him straight in the eye and lied most beautifully. 'No,' I said calmly, thinking about all those glorious fivers wrapped up in a pair of Sophie's plastic pants and hidden away in the nappy drawer, 'I'm just learning to manage things a bit better.'

Chapter 2

The bank statement was so awful that I ran away from it across the road and into Jean's house. Sophie and I sat crumbling rusks over the freshly vacuumed carpet while Jean ironed Kevin's shirts.

'I've got to make a fortune fast,' I said, and then I had a vision. I said, 'I've just had a vision of hundreds of old ladies and housewives and unemployed lecturers, all sitting at home all day, making things.'

'What sort of things?' asked Jean, adjusting her steamer.

'Oh, you know – teddy bears and gonks and bookmarks and things. We could be their outlet. Just think. All those creative people, starving in their homes, knee deep in teddy bears and gonks, simply waiting for us to come along and sell them.'

Jean ironed on thoughtfully. 'It'll have to be sale or return,' she said at last. 'My housekeeping won't stretch to capital outlay.' That's why I need Jean. She uses phrases like capital outlay and sale or return.

'We can have a market stall,' I said. 'I'll ask Roger to make us a trestle table, and we'll go to Tarminster market and make our fortunes.' Roger is my husband. He's very tolerant and useful and he gave up all hope of having meals cooked for him, or socks washed, years ago. Jean said she didn't think she'd mention it to Kevin yet. Kevin's on the career ladder and he likes his underpants ironed and his meals on time.

We put an advertisement in the local paper. It read: 'Do you make things at home? Would you like to sell them for a profit? If so, ring us.'

The telephone never stopped ringing and three days later I had a list of forty old ladies and unemployed lecturers to visit. Sophie and the pram and I set out at half past nine on the fourth morning and covered about three square miles. We lurched home loaded with stuffed bears, stuffed gonks, stuffed draught excluders, shell pictures, crinoline lavatory paper holders and fifty pressed flower bookmarks.

In the meantime Jean was being administrative. She telephoned the market supervisor at Tarminster and booked us a pitch for the following Tuesday.

'D'you think Kevin would lend us his car on Tuesday and go to work by bus?' I asked her.

She went a bit pale. 'I'll work on him.'

I don't know what she did or said – perhaps she ironed his socks or something – but somehow she persuaded him to lend us the car. 'He says he'll work at home today,' she whispered when I went to collect her, 'he's not very happy about it though.'

We lashed the trestle table and the pram on the roof-rack and wedged Sophie into the back seat with the bears, gonks and draught excluders. Jean turned the ignition key. Nothing happened. A quarter of an hour later she was still turning the key and the car was full of an awful smell of petrol. 'I've flooded it,' she said. 'It always happens when I'm nervous.'

I slunk out of the car and tapped gently on Jean's front door. When Kevin saw me his face went tight. 'I'm terribly sorry, Kevin,' I muttered, 'but we can't start the car.' Kevin flared his nostrils but he didn't say anything. He rolled back his cuffs very carefully, walked to the car and gave it a push. We rolled it down the hill towards the river and at the last minute the engine spat and fired and we were off. Jean and I began to giggle.

When we got to Tarminster we untied the pram and strapped Sophie inside it. Then we set up the trestle and arranged our wares. They looked irresistible but somehow the shoppers of Tarminster managed to resist them. The market supervisor came to collect our pitch fee, it began to rain and Sophie was getting bored and hungry. So we packed everything up and drove home. The adventure had cost us two pounds in petrol, two pounds in pitch fees and we hadn't sold a single bookmark.

I couldn't bring myself to disappoint all those creative people so I bought their creations with the next week's housekeeping money – which is why my overdraft has doubled, why our living room is full of stuffed toys and shell pictures, and why all our friends and relations will get draught excluders and gonks every Christmas for the rest of their lives.

I'm afraid it's also why Kevin has put his and Jean's house up for sale and is looking for a more rising-executive sort of neighbourhood. But there's a glint in Jean's eye which wasn't there before . . . and I think I saw Kevin ironing his own underpants the other day.

Chapter 3

I crouched, hunched with boredom, at the end of the bath, watching Sophie emptying boatfuls of water over her head and spooning spadefuls of bubbles into her mouth. 'Water,' she remarked.

'I know,' I said. 'What you're doing is called water play. It's good for you. I just wish it wasn't so bad for me.'

I'd been through it all before with the other two, ten years earlier. Water play, pastry play, earth play, throwing-the-furniture-over-the-room play. All that playing which is so educationally vital if you are under five, and so rivetingly boring if you are over twenty-five. I'd read the right books and mixed with the right parents. I knew that if I didn't stimulate their whirring little brains before they were five, they'd never make it to university, but maybe that wouldn't be such a bad thing. Maybe then they wouldn't mind so much when their turn came to rear the next generation of women.

'I feel like a horse that's being broken in,' I said to Sophie. 'How long should I make your lunging rein, would you suggest?' She pulled out the plug and we went downstairs for Art. She stuck all the green wax crayons up her nose and fed the others to Mistake, the dog. I crawled sadly round the table legs rescuing what bits I could, while Mistake licked one of my ears and Sophie licked the other.

It was pouring with rain, but anything was better than

being educational indoors, so I strapped Sophie into the pram, put the choke-chain on Mistake and hurtled out into the weather. I parked them all outside the Post Office and went in to buy a stamp. When I came out again, Sophie was dangling from the pram by her lunging rein and Mistake was nearly strangling herself on the choke-chain. I hauled Sophie back into position, but she immediately dived out again. I realised that she'd outgrown the pram. I walked home, composing a 'pram for sale' advertisement. 'There must be something you can do that I can do as well,' I said to Sophie. 'There must be something we could both enjoy doing together.' She laughed and tore up the *Radio Times*. Something clicked in my head and I remembered papier-mâché puppet heads. I looked at the pram and saw how it could be converted into a mobile puppet booth. I dreamed a daydream of show business and fame and fortune, and that was how the Perambulating Puppet Theatre was born.

All afternoon, Sophie and I sat happily at the kitchen table and shredded old newspapers into the washing-up bowl. I poured kettles of boiling water over the paper and Sophie waved a wooden spoon. We kneaded and squeezed and pounded and wrung until we'd achieved a dark grey, sludgy porridge. Then we dashed out into the wind and rain again to buy wallpaper paste. We mixed up the paste in a jamjar and poured it into the pulp. Then we each scooped up a fistful of porridge and began to model heads.

For weeks after that, anyone who dropped by for a cup of tea found herself stuck to my kitchen table, pulping paper. It became an occupational therapy for all the housewives in our street. Meals were forgotten, potties went unemptied, beds were left unmade and carpets unhoovered, but puppets rose up and multiplied on window-sills and on radiators, in airing cupboards and in gas cookers. Husbands and older children looked reproachful and neglected. Mine caught colds and chickenpox which shortened my lunging rein, tightened my choke-chain and made me feel guilty.

In spite of it all, the puppet heads hardened and dried and were painted in brilliant gold and greens and reds. I produced a play called 'The Miraculous Apple Tree', about a farmer whose apple tree bears the finest fruit in the neighbourhood, and so all the neighbours come and steal it. The farmer asks God to make the tree sticky; God agrees, and all the thieves, including Death and the Devil, get stuck. It's a medieval miracle play, and it used to tour the market places of Holland in the fifteenth century. I toured it to the Sunday morning market in our village hall and set up the booth between a goats' cheese stall and a bookseller. Just as God was agreeing to make the tree sticky, his head flew off, bounced on to a pram wheel and rolled under the goats' cheese stall. Sophie scrambled after it and got it back, but I couldn't stick it back on in the middle of the miracle, so God had to carry on with a piece of quarter-inch dowelling sticking up where his head should have been.

That evening I was bathing Sophie and trying to work out a way of sticking the head back securely when Jane, my twelve-year-old, came storming into the bathroom waving her maths homework at me.

'I just don't get this,' she raged. 'It's a stupid book. It's full of stupid unnecessary problems.'

'So is life,' I raged back, 'and you'd better get used to it.' I felt horribly ashamed of myself after she'd gone. I'd snapped at her because my choke-chain was too tight. I lifted Sophie out of the bath, wrapped her in a towel and went in search of Jane. 'Sorry,' I said. 'That was awful. I shouldn't have shouted at you. I'm meant to be here to help you with your homework. It's my job.'

Jane looked up from her book and she wasn't being reproachful or neglected any more. 'We're not your only job,' she said. 'You mustn't give up now. If you stop now, there's no point in me doing my maths or anything else, is there? You'll be letting us all down if you give up now.'

The choke-chain and lunging rein fell off and disappeared. I wasn't failing them after all. They didn't want me to be cosy and contented all the time, they wanted me to break through to other things. I flung my arms around Jane and solved the stupid unnecessary maths problem in two seconds. Then I dried Sophie off and worked at the perfect way to make sure God's head would never fall off again.

Chapter 4

Nola Gleeson, ex-aquabelle and dancer, lived with her poodle in a peeling first-floor flat next door to us. She moved in there when she retired from the water and took up religion, and her bedroom window was looped with pink ribbons and hand-written texts proclaiming 'The Word Was Made Flesh' or 'Love Thy Neighbour' – they changed from week to week, according to her mood.

Nola's hair and lips were a matching red, her eyeshadow was aquamarine and her voice was an evangelical shriek. She loved Sophie, and was always offering to look after her while I went shopping. I took her up on it one day, but got back to find Sophie gnawing a cigarette and a gin-soaked poodle asleep in the cot.

Nola was a good neighbour though. She never complained about our milk bottles or the state of the dustbin and it was comforting to know that my sins would be forgiven me. One morning I was pushing Sophie past Nola's railings when I heard a tapping at her window. 'Love Thy Neighbour' was tilting slowly over to one side as the curtain quivered and a green face loomed out at me.

'Darling,' she croaked, 'can you do me a favour? I'm not feeling very well today and I've run out of pills. Pop into Mr Percival's and ask him for another lot for me.' She lurched forward a little and the straps of her black lace nightie flapped sadly round her shoulders.

'OK Nola,' I called, 'I'll be back in ten minutes.' I hurried along to Percival's the chemist's and jumped the queue. 'Excuse me, Mr Percival,' I gasped, 'I've just seen Nola Gleeson. She says she's ill and she looks awful. Can I take her some more of her pills?'

A funny sort of silence stretched back through the shop, and Mr Percival looked mournful and Scottish. 'I can't do that, my dear,' he said. 'She's got to bring in the prescription.' He looked at me gently over his pince-nez. 'If I were you I wouldn't get involved, I wouldn't let my wife go into that place, and you certainly don't want to take the baby in there.' He paused and leant across the counter. 'Drink and drugs, you know,' he said, and sniffed. 'You don't know what you'll find.'

I couldn't think what to do. I pushed Sophie slowly back to Nola's window and peered up to where 'Love Thy Neighbour' still leaned wearily on its left elbow. There was no sign of Nola.

To get to her first floor, you had to plunge down the yard steps into the basement and brave a concrete tunnel leading to the lavatorially tiled inside steps that climbed coldly up to Nola's door. I unstrapped Sophie and stuffed her under one arm and then started down the steps. I could hear the poodle whining and yapping, and I felt sick. She'd probably collapsed in her lacy black nightie and would be lying there under 'Love Thy Neighbour' and I wouldn't know what to do. I was shivering when we reached her door and Sophie kept saying 'Dog, dog' and grizzling.

To my enormous relief, the door was locked. 'Nola,' I called, but there was no reply. I went home and phoned the police.

The policeman who answered wasn't very worried. 'She's probably just sleeping it off,' he said cheerfully. 'Keep an eye on the window and give us a ring tomorrow if nothing's changed.'

Nothing changed. By nine o'clock that evening I couldn't stand it any longer and I crept back down the steps. The concrete tunnel was awful in the dark. I pressed a switch which turned a light bulb on for fifteen seconds, and got me to the bottom of the inside stairs. As soon as I started to climb them, I was plunged into darkness again. I found another time switch and pressed it with a shaking finger. The light went out twice more before I stood outside Nola's door again and heard the poodle whimpering. I called, 'Nola! Nola?' There was no reply.

It was a different policeman who answered the phone this time and he was angry. 'We've got more important things to do than wake up drunk old women,' he growled, and rang off.

The next day, on my way back from the shops, I saw the police car and the ambulance parked outside the railings. I hurried indoors and stayed there for an hour. I didn't want to see them carrying her corpse into the ambulance. Later I went to Mr Percival's to buy some nappy liners.

'Have you heard about Nola Gleeson?' he asked. 'They've pumped her out and cleaned her up. They'll be sending her home tomorrow.'

I was amazed. 'You mean she isn't dead?'

'Good heavens, no. She never is. She does this every six months or so and comes back good as new.'

Next day Sophie and I walked past Nola's window. 'Love Thy Neighbour' had disappeared and 'Piss Off' stood in its place. I stood there staring at it until a furious screech came at me through the curtains.

'You bloody interfering cow,' shrieked Nola Gleeson, 'don't you ever get the ambulance to me again and don't go sticking your snooty nose in where it's not wanted.'

I shot off up the street with curses spitting after me. 'Bye, bye,' said Sophie.

'Piss Off' stayed in the window for a fortnight. I went

another way to the shops. Then, one fine morning, there came a knocking at the door and Nola Gleeson stood there smiling, with a grubby toy rabbit in her hand. 'Hello, my love,' she said. 'I've brought a present for the baby.' The 'Piss Off' sign had gone and in its place a bright red notice shouted: 'Purge me with Hyssop (Ps:51).'

I looked up 'hyssop' in the dictionary. It said, 'A small, bushy aromatic plant, formerly used in medicine as a purgative.'

'Have you got any hyssop?' I asked Mr Percival, next time I went in for gripe water.

He looked at me and raised an eyebrow. 'Am I my brother's keeper?' he inquired.

Chapter 5

'The most awful thing about being me or you is the way everybody needs us all the time,' said Jean glumly as we washed up the elevenses to clear space for the lunchtime rush which would gallop us into the lunchtime wash-up to make room for the home-from-school-what's-for-tea-I-can't-do-my-maths-homework panic.

'The most awful thing about being me,' I said, 'is that when by some mistake I do get an hour to myself, I can't think what on earth I want to do, and I can't even remember what it was I used to like doing.'

I hoovered the crumbs while Sophie emptied the compost bucket, pulled saucepans out of the cupboard and chewed old potato peelings.

Jean sighed. 'I'll have to go home and get Kevin's lunch in a minute,' she said.

I stood still. 'I wonder what they'd do if we just weren't there one day?'

Jean shrugged, and replied, 'Probably go to the pub for a pie.'

'So why don't we?' I asked.

'No money,' said Jean. She was right. We'd just spent it all on tea-bags and liver.

'I've still got my horse-racing money,' I confessed, 'but I was saving that for something really big, like a holiday or a car.' We dreamed for a moment about the beauty and freedom of having our own car, but had to face the fact that my hundred pound gambling win wasn't going to buy us anything that would actually move.

'There's not really a lot of point in having a car that can't go anywhere,' said Jean sadly.

Then Sophie got her finger jammed down a saucepan handle and after I'd unstuck her it was time to slice the liver and chop the onions. Jean went home to be wifely and I kicked the Hoover.

Lunch was over and I was washing it up. Sophie tugged at my skirt and grinned as her own personal and familiar farmyard stench drifted up into my nostrils. We trudged upstairs. I changed her and wandered down again to finish the washing up. 'What I really need,' I explained to her as she emptied the saucepan cupboard again, 'is a bit of time and space for myself, somewhere I can go to remember what it was like when I was just me. It's not that I don't love you more than anything else in the world, but I think there used to be a time when I wasn't only blotting-paper.' She looked understanding and chewed the floorcloth thoughtfully. The phone rang.

It was Jean. 'I've just worked out what it is I need!' she shouted. 'It's a bit of time and space to . . .' Sophie sat on the phone and cut us off.

We went shopping and stopped as usual outside the post office to read the notices. 'Home wanted for two guinea-pigs', 'Fish tank for sale', 'Child-minder needed for Nancy (three) and Zebedee (eighteen months)', 'Four-berth caravan for sale, not suitable for towing. Wood stove. No site. One hundred pounds'. I stared at the board and my heart beat as if I were outside the Delphic Oracle. There was certainly no point in a car that didn't move, but a caravan that didn't move was altogether different.

I whizzed round the shops like a woman possessed. One hundred pounds. I'd got a hundred pounds wrapped in a pair of plastic pants in Sophie's nappy drawer. No site. No site. Where could I find a site? Jenkins' Farm, just outside the village. Surely Mike Jenkins would have a little space for a four-berth caravan unsuitable for towing, with wood stove. I raced the pram along the road to Jenkins' Farm. Mike Jenkins wasn't there, but Susie his wife was. Her face lit up at the thought of a bolt-hole with a wood stove and she said she'd find a corner of a field rent-free and could she play too? We rushed round to tell Jean and I telephoned the number on the advertisement. I made an appointment, unearthed my winnings from the nappy drawer and went off to inspect my daydream.

She was beautiful. Very old, dark blue with a chimney and gas brackets and her name was 'Shangri-la'. I handed over my hundred pounds and Susie Jenkins pinched a tractor when Mike wasn't looking and we towed our bit of time and space into its final resting place.

Susie has Tuesdays, I have Wednesdays and Jean has Thursdays. The one who goes to Shangri-la divides her children between the other two, and nobody else knows where she's gone or what she's doing. Sometimes I read a book, once I wrote the first page of a book, and sometimes I just sit and think. That was very difficult at first. Jean's installed her spinning wheel and a bag of fleece, and Susie won't say what she's up to. But if the wind is blowing in the right direction on her days in Shangri-la, you can hear strumming noises and Joan Baez songs coming across the fields. Susie Jenkins is learning to play the guitar.

We don't cook lunch on Shangri-la days and we don't tell our husbands why. Roger came home one day and said he'd met Mike Jenkins outside the pub at lunchtime. Apparently Mike is furious because Susie's let some awful hippie women dump a tatty old caravan in the corner of one of his fields. 'Funny,' said Roger, 'I didn't think Susie

Jenkins was that type at all. She always seems so sensible and reliable.'

'Very odd,' I said, 'but you never can tell about people, can you?' And I gave him his lunch in a devoted sort of way.

Chapter 6

I hate the kitchen floor. I hated it so much one Friday that I left it crawling stickily round the table's ankles and tried to read a book instead. But wherever I went there were toys and crumbs and unmade beds and dirty sheets and unfed cats and unwashed nappies. I shut my eyes, ran a hot bath and climbed in with the book.

It was a very wise and spiritual book about Indian dance. It said that the True Soul Of The Nation's Dance rises up like an act of worship out of the everyday activities of ordinary people. I lay there in the steam thinking about the chaos downstairs and wondering what had happened to my Dancing Soul.

Then I got out of the bath and dripped downstairs to the kitchen, where I danced The Dance Of The Washing Of The Floor. It goes like this:

You kneel on the floor in an attitude of prayer, holding a wet floorcloth high above your head, and you make a high-pitched humming noise through your nose. You bend in the middle until your forehead touches the floor, then you come up again to the kneeling position. You repeat that three times, after which you'll be dizzy, your knees will tingle, and you'll have a black mark on your forehead.

Next you make a slow, strong wringing movement with your hands, so that the water from the floorcloth drips on to your head and into your eyes. You lean forward slowly and sweep the cloth in an arc from left to right and back again. Your high-pitched nasal hum should change to a 'shoosh-shoosh-shoosh' in time with the semi-circular sweep.

I'd just got that far when there was a knock at the door and Jean walked into the kitchen. 'Dear God,' she said. 'Do you need a doctor?'

I explained about expressing the Nation's Soul, and she thought it was a good idea, except that I'd have done better to have my bath after the flooral dance and not before it. 'I'm going shopping,' she said. 'Do you and Sophie want to come?' I potted Sophie unsuccessfully and we set off for the Co-op.

It was full of senior citizens and depressed-looking women buying frozen peas and one-size tights. Sophie and I were loitering by the lavatory cleaners when we heard a strange rhythmic wailing coming from the far side of the deep freeze. I hurried round, to see Jean stretching up on to her right toes while her left hand plucked daintily at a tin of rice pudding on the top shelf. As she stretched she wailed 'Ri-i-ice,' came down into a crouching position with both feet planted squarely on the Co-op lino, and grunted 'Pud'. Then she flew up again, this time on her left toes while the right hand grabbed a tin of tomatoes.

The housewives and senior citizens stared phlegmatically ahead of them. Not one even blinked. I poked Jean in the ribs on her next upward reach. 'Don't be such a show-off,' I whispered.

She was hurt. 'What about the True Soul Of The Nation?' she asked.

'Deep frozen,' I said. 'Come on, let's go home.'

So we escaped from the Co-op and went home. I tried to pot Sophie again while Jean read my book. 'It says here that you ought to have an Auspicious Pot as an offering to the Gods,' she announced. 'Come on Sophie, this isn't just a question of potty-training, it's a religious act.' Sophie smiled and fell off.

I'd just invented a new dance called The Changing Of The Nappy. You pick up one corner with your finger and thumb and fold it into the centre while balancing on the opposite foot. Then with a tiger-like spring you swap hands and feet and fold in the other corner. I was doing this beautifully and soulfully when Jean shouted, 'Look out!' and shoved the Auspicious Pot across to me. Sophie was going bright red and grunting. I grabbed her and plonked her on the pot just in time. 'You're a very, very clever girl,' I told her and then we went downstairs to do The Dance Of The Fish Fingers for her dinner.

Chapter 7

I was feeling in need of a little intellectual stimulation and a lot of cash, so when Glenda Dawson, the deputy head of the school where I once worked, rang up and said that the Geography master had gone on a course on Meaningful Confrontation and could I do a day's supply, I said yes.

I left Roger and Sophie supplied with disposable nappies and instant foods and drove off to school.

Glenda was frowning at the timetable, chewing her pen and muttering, while her pet duck emptied the waste paper basket all over her office. 'Two more have gone sick today,' she said. 'So I'll give you a mixture of things. You've got double English with 3J for a start, God help you. You can borrow my duck if you like.'

Glenda's duck is a Visual Aid. She'd rescued it from a river when it was a backward and neglected duckling unloved by its mother. It promptly imprinted itself on her and followed her everywhere, quacking and fluffing its feathers and providing stimulus for creative writing in English lessons.

I marched into 3J's classroom, duck at the ready. 'Not that bloody duck again,' somebody groaned. I realised that I'd have to re-think.

'What have you been doing in your English lessons so far?' I asked brightly.

'Describing that duck,' shouted 3J.

'All right. Now you can describe each other. Look carefully at your neighbour for ten minutes, then write down what you see. No talking please.'

They didn't talk. They shrieked, laughed, mouth-popped, farted and yawned. At last they settled down and began to write, and the duck and I strolled around the classroom looking over shoulders and behind ears and under armpits. 'Wayne Foggin is a spotty-faced big-eared gitt.' I looked at Wayne Foggin and had to agree. 'Git only has one "t",' I pointed out and moved on.

The bell rang. One lesson gone, one more to go. How on earth would I keep them occupied for forty more minutes? But the bell rang on and on and on and with joy in my heart I recognised the fire alarm.

'Don't panic,' I said to 3J. 'Take your bags and file out quietly and calmly down the stairs and out past the gym.' With shrieks of excitement they crushed through the doorway and roared down the corridor. I closed the windows, collected the register, locked the door and followed. 3J was lined up in the playground. All the girls were present, and I started on the boys.

'Jeffrey Arnold.' 'Yes, Miss.'

'Nicholas Bishop.' 'Yes, Miss.'

All present until: 'Wayne Foggin.' No reply.

'Wayne Foggin?'

'He's not here, Miss.'

At the same moment it dawned on me that I'd forgotten the duck. Edgar Godfrey, a keen probationer, was standing nearby, ticking off 4L on the register.

'Keep an eye on 3J, will you?' I said. 'I've got to pop upstairs and get something.'

Edgar went pale. 'You can't go inside the building,' he squawked. 'This isn't just a practice, it's a bomb scare. Someone phoned in and said they'd planted something. We've got to wait till the police arrive.' I felt terrible. I'd left Wayne Foggin and the duck to be blown to Bombay, and even worse than that, I'd locked them in.

I had no choice. I ran round to the front of the building and in through the main doors. Nobody saw me because they were all counting children at the back. I was terrified. Every kit bag seemed to tick, every anorak concealed a lethal-looking throbbing lump. Sweating and dizzy I climbed the stairs to 3J's classroom, unlocked the door and found Wayne Foggin and the duck weeping in each other's arms. I scooped them both up and fled to the playground. 'Why did you stay behind?' I shouted.

He wailed loudly. 'I'm not a spotty-faced big-eared git,' he sobbed.

'No, of course you're not. You're a hero. You saved Miss Dawson's duck,' I said.

Glenda wandered over to collect her duck. 'What a bore,' she said. 'Everybody knows that the phone call was from Conger Eeles in the fifth form. We excluded him last week, so he's getting his revenge.' I remembered the ticking kit bags and pulsating anoraks and felt very silly.

After break I taught Drama with much humming and heavy breathing and imagining we were passing something nasty round in a circle. After dinner I taught Health and Social, which was about The Population Explosion and which 4L put down to More People Doing It More Often. I couldn't argue about that either.

I drove home wondering why on earth anybody needed to go on a short course on Meaningful Confrontation. I'd rather go to one on the Care of Ducks.

Chapter 8

I was surprised when Kevin knocked on my door and asked if he could come in and talk. Kevin's never liked me much. In fact, he's never liked me at all. He thinks it's my fault that Jean's not as well-trained as she used to be. I invited him in. 'Aren't you at work today?' I asked.

'Obviously not,' replied Kevin. He didn't seem to know what to say next, so I chatted emptily until he snapped, 'I've just given in my notice.' I was speechless. Kevin was a Rising Executive, a clean, detached man in his middle thirties, dedicated to nice cars and patios and getting on. I'd never understood why Jean married him. We had often discussed this mystery. 'I expect you're wondering why Jean ever married me,' said Kevin.

'No, no,' I lied.

'When I met her, she was young and bright and studying domestic science at the tech. She seemed to like me being masterful and organising things. We got married and I gave her the housekeeping every week. We bought a little house, we had the children and we bought a bigger house.'

'With a patio,' I murmured.

Kevin looked hurt. 'I got promoted and bought a new car and I thought everything was fine. But then it all changed. Jean got moody and she seemed to resent cooking my meals and ironing my shirts.' There was a pause.

'When did you notice the change?' I asked.

'Soon after you moved here,' said Kevin.

I had a moment of clear-sightedness. 'She's under-achieving,' I said. 'We all are. We grow up and train for careers and learn to be stimulated, but at the same time we want to love and breed. We feel like setting fire to things or mugging toddlers, but we're too well brought up to do that, so we scream at our children and blame our husbands for not providing us with the excitement we'd learned to need before we married them.'

'She told me she was bored,' said Kevin sadly. 'She told me she was bored because we were boring. Then she said she wasn't going to spend the rest of her life being bored and boring and I'd better do something about it.'

'So you went and gave in your notice?'

'Yes,' said Kevin, 'I never wanted to be an executive anyway. I was only doing it for her and the children. At least she can't accuse me of being reliable.'

There was another silence.

'Have you any idea of what you want to do instead of middle management?' I asked.

Kevin blushed. 'I want to be a woodcarver,' he said.

He walked out of the house, climbed into his nice shiny car and drove away.

Jean arrived an hour later, looking white and sleepless. 'I had a terrible row with Kevin last night. I told him he was boring and he'd got to do something about it.'

'And did he?' I asked carefully.

'I shouldn't think so. He's too bloody reliable.'

This was awful. He'd told me before he'd told her. 'How could Kevin become less boring, do you think?' I asked cautiously.

'Oh, I dunno,' said Jean crossly. 'I wish he'd go away and be a drag queen or a spaceman or something.'

'Oh, that's all right then,' – I was enormously relieved – 'he's going to be a woodcarver.'

Jean was quiet for a moment, then she burst into tears. 'What about the mortgage?' she wailed.

It took them a few months to sort it out and I kept out of the way until they'd done so. Jean didn't come for coffee any more and I didn't dare to ring her.

Then, one morning, when I was walking back from the shops, she drove past me in a second-hand van with 'Kevin Cummings, Woodcarver' written all over one side of it. On the other side was written 'Jean Cummings, Caterer'. I got in and Jean drove me to their home. Kevin had turned his patio into a workshop. He was sitting at a bench carving a wooden giraffe and he smiled when he saw me. He'd never done that before.

Jean explained what had happened over coffee in her catering kitchen. 'When you told me that Kevin wanted to be a woodcarver, I was furious. I went home and shouted at him, "What about me and the children and the house and the food and the clothes?" But he said he wanted to try this more than anything else in the world. Then he said, "Isn't there something you've always really wanted to do?" There was, but I didn't dare tell him what it was. But I remembered an idea I'd once had about starting up my own catering business, so I told him about that and it's working and here it is. We sold the car and bought the van and converted the patio, and Kevin carves his toys and sells them to local shops and I do weddings and funerals and christenings and business lunches and things.'

I walked home slowly, remembering the times that Jean and I had grumbled about the tedium of life and marriage and motherhood. I got down on my hands and knees and wrung the floorcloth out again, gazing into the bucket of hot water and waiting for it to give me a clue about my own life and what it was I really wanted to do with it. Did I really want to change things? Did I really want to be a bank manager or a business woman or a politician? Not in the least. Did I want to be a dancer, or a trapeze artiste or a spaceman or the Queen? Of course I did. I wanted to be all of them. And an engine driver and a pirate and a jockey and a spy and a racing car driver. So did we all, all those of us who hadn't grown up and who still dreamed dreams.

I shook myself and laughed and put my hands back into the bucket. I knew who I was. I was the mother of my children, the wife of my husband, the maker of my home. The chances of becoming a spaceman or a spy were remote. I might as well stop griping and get on with the kitchen floor.

Chapter 9

'You are fourteen,' I said to Jane through the bathroom keyhole, 'and there is absolutely no way that I am going to let you go to a party on the other side of town unless I know where it is. And unless I come and pick you up at the end of it.' The door opened and she dripped out in a cloud of steam and damp towels.

'You're so over-protective,' she snapped, vanishing into the airing cupboard and pulling everything down on to the floor. 'Nobody else's mother makes such a fuss about everything. All my friends' mothers trust them.'

I knew that line and countered it with the usual speech that it wasn't her that I didn't trust and it wasn't that I didn't trust her and it wasn't I who didn't trust her, and by the time I had finished, she had crossed from the airing cupboard into her bedroom, leaving a trail of wet foot-prints and no sign that she had heard me behind her. I carried on negotiations through a crack in her bedroom door, and in the end we reached a sullen truce. She would give me the address and phone number of the party house as long as I promised not to look at it and to pin it face down on the kitchen notice board and only turn it over for use in a fearful emergency. I would be allowed to drive her to the party (she hadn't got the bus fare) as long as I stopped at the street corner and dropped her off without smiling or speaking or in any way indicating that I might be related to her. And at midnight, I would be at the same street corner and so would she and if she wasn't I would come to the house and collect her.

I pinned the address face down on the notice board, put Sophie to bed, left Roger and Harriet with pot noodles in front of the telly and drove Jane, in granite silence, to the party street corner. I parked, she got out and swung away down the street in her mini-skirt. As she drew level with the gate of the party house, a youth lurched out and was hideously sick in the gutter. Jane didn't waver. Without a wave or a backward glance at me, she strode into the house and disappeared. For a moment, my maternal instincts switched on to the vomiting youth, but I beat them down. I started the engine and became aware of three other discreetly parked cars and three other anxious-looking parents who gazed down the pavement as their offspring sauntered nonchalantly to the party. I drove home, thinking about waltzes and quicksteps and young men who had said 'May I have the pleasure of this dance?' I looked at the rest of my family lolling over empty pot noodle pots in front of a sex-and-violence soap, and wondered if anyone would ever say 'May I have the pleasure of this dance?' to anyone ever again. The soap thrashed and screamed its way to another crisis and I tried to blot out the pictures that slid into my mind of Jane surrounded by flashing lights and vomiting youths and drug-pushers.

At a quarter past eleven, I got into the car and drove the four miles into town to Jane's street corner. The road sloped downhill to the party house, and as I pulled into the curb, I saw two girls come running out, one of them chasing the other with some sharp instrument. The chaser was barefoot, and as they drew level with me, she caught her quarry, leapt upon her and pulled her to the ground, jabbing at her with the sharp thing which I now could see was a stiletto heel. The girls rolled back down the hill in a tangled fury of hair, curses, tights and mini-skirts. It was a quarter to twelve and too early for Jane to appear. I hummed 'Some Enchanted Evening' desperately and watched the police arrive to disentangle the knot of hair, nails, mini-skirts and legs which was still thrashing around in the road.

Then they had gone and Jane was walking up the street towards me. I stayed in the car and pretended not to notice when she slid into the passenger seat and closed the door. Other girls and boys slid awkwardly in beside other parents on other street corners.

'Good party?' I enquired.

'Brilliant,' said Jane, and I drove her home and locked and bolted the front door against the outside world.

But you can't keep the world outside for long. Sooner or later it will seep through the letter box and the cracks in the wood and the gap under the door. Our family life was turning into another screaming soap opera.

Episode One happened one Monday morning, when Jane was fifteen, Harriet was fourteen and Sophie was nearly four. The first shriek, which tore me out of sleep, was followed by the slam of a door and a furious thumping. I lurched out of bed and along the landing to find Harriet, naked except for a towel wrapped around her dripping head, battering clenched fists against the bathroom door. 'I was in there first,' she yelled. 'I only went to find a towel and she got in. Come out now, you frigging cow, I was in there first.' It was six o'clock in the morning. Loud showering noises and Radio One fought each other behind the locked door. 'Jane!' shrieked Harriet again, 'come out. I've got to get to school.' I stood aghast, listening to my home turning into a battlefield.

Roger appeared in the bedroom doorway, ominous in pyjamas. 'It is six o'clock in the morning. If there is one more sound from you two, the bathroom will be banned for a week.' Nothing can be more terrible to a teenage daughter than a banned bathroom. Harriet slammed into her bedroom and I followed Roger into ours.

Ten minutes later, I heard the bathroom door swing open and Jane and Radio One paddling out on to the landing and into her room. Then Harriet's door creaked open and I guessed what was going to happen. I slid out of bed and crept across the landing to Jane's door. By pressing an ear to the door, I could hear the whispered warfare.

'What the shaggin' hell do you think you're wearing?'

'A shaggin' mini-skirt.'

The fight broke the surface again, tearing the morning still further apart.

I opened the door. 'Where did you learn language like that?' I demanded.

'From you,' said Jane, and returned to the quarrel which was about a very boring-looking black mini-skirt which had been lying, harmless and ignored for weeks, behind the airing-cupboard tank.

'I know it's mine because the label's still on mine,' shouted Jane.

'There's no label on this one.' Harriet's voice and chin were stubborn and both her hands were behind her, fiddling with the waistband of the skirt.

I began to say something about it being wrong to lie and steal.

'You keep out of this,' flared Harriet.

I wasn't taking that and I reached out to grab the skirt. Harriet hung on, I pulled, and the slit in the side of the skirt tore right up to the waistband and the label.

'Now look what you've done,' said Jane.

Sophie climbed sleepily out of her bunk and stomped downstairs. I could hear her emptying her toybox and discussing something with Mistake, and I remembered the years when Jane and Harriet had built dens together out of chairs and hearthrugs, had written letters to toothfairies, mashed up magic potions from flower petals, held jumble sales in aid of threatened wildlife, wept when their best friends had betrayed them and come to me for comfort and clean knickers. I dropped my end of the torn skirt and turned away from them.

Sophie plodded back up the stairs, trailing her dressing-gown belt and holding something out to me. 'What's this?' she asked. 'I found it at the bottom of the toybox.' It was a pack of 'Happy Families' cards.

Then Jane was sixteen, Harriet was fifteen and Sophie was nearly five. It was as well that I'd kept the letter which said 'Daer Tooth Faery, my tooth fell down the drane on my way home from school I hop that counts love from Jane' and the one which said 'Daer Mistake, I hope you like it at Cennals I miss you very much lots and lots and lots of love from Harriet.' Otherwise I would have believed that they had never been children, had never loved us or home, had never done anything but quarrel and go to discos.

Jane never spoke to us at all unless she had to, and she never ever smiled, except at the telephone or at a series of boys who were all called Jaz and Chas and Baz and who passed me shiftily and silently in the hall on their way up to Jane's bedroom floor. When she wasn't talking to Jaz or Baz or Chas, she was permanently wired to the telephone or to her walkman.

One afternoon, I came in wearily after a day's supply teaching. Sophie was tired and grizzly, there was no food in the fridge, the breakfast washing up was still in the sink, fluff and crumbs from the day before were still on the carpet and Jane was still on the telephone. I waited ten minutes before I interrupted to ask politely whether her animated conversation – 'He doesn't, does he? No, he didn't did he? I don't believe it' – was on their phone bill or ours. 'Shit, I can't talk now, my mother's just come in. I'll have to go.' She rang off and ran up to her room, muttering about the lack of privacy and respect in the house. I decided to be assertive and said that I needed some help with the washing up and she could choose whether to wash or dry. Silently, furiously, she stalked into the kitchen and turned on the tap. 'The water's cold.' The tone implied that it was entirely my fault for being incompetent and that the great mind of an 'A' level literature student should be allowed to be above the mundanities of food and washing up. I happened to be holding half a scooped-out melon skin in my hand, and the something in her voice made me lift the melon high and plonk it neatly on top of her shampooed head. She gazed at me in outraged disbelief and I began to laugh. She snatched the melon off her head and fled upstairs, and I, realising that I had gone too far, ran after her. On the landing at the top of the stairs was the dirty linen basket, full and overflowing. Jane reached it, picked it up, turned and hurled it down the stairs at me. Then she rushed into her bedroom and slammed the door. I could hear her sobbing on the other side. I knocked, but she wouldn't let me in, so I went downstairs and finished the washing up miserably on my own. I heard her run down the stairs and slam the front door behind her and I didn't know what to do. She and I were so far apart now. In the end, I picked up the dirty washing and stuffed it into the machine and then I went and changed the sheets on her bed.

'Why are you crying, Mum?' asked Sophie. I said I wasn't crying, I was cutting up onions for Spaghetti Bolognese. Spaghetti Bolognese is good if you don't know whether you are cooking supper for five or for four. It turned out to be four. Jane didn't come home for supper, and by eleven thirty, the family deadline for the last bus or the telephone call to say where you were, I was frantic. I prowled the house like a caged animal, leafing through the telephone book, wishing that Jaz and Chas and Baz had surnames, rushing to the window every time I heard a car pull up. At half past midnight, just as I was about to ring the police, a taxi drew up and I heard Jane's footsteps walking up the path to the front door. I hid in the dark of the living room so that she wouldn't think I'd waited up for her, and wept with relief as I heard her climb the stairs and go into the bathroom.

In the morning, she said, 'Thanks for the clean sheets, Mum,' and smiled.

Chapter 10

Strange snuffling noises were coming from the airing cupboard. Had Mistake got shut in there again? Had the hamster escaped and was it shredding all my tights? I opened the door and saw Harriet wrapped in one towel with her face buried in another, shaking with sobs. The fifteen years since she had been born melted away as I put my arms round her. 'What on earth is the matter?'

'Nothing.' Another huge sob shuddered through her and she pulled away from me.

'I thought you were Mistake,' I said, for something to say.

'I am a mistake. My whole life's a mistake,' said Harriet angrily. Her eyes had gone small and pink and her nose was swollen from crying and I thought what a lot of rubbish they tell us in fairy tales when the princess becomes even lovelier when she weeps. Most of us look like boiled pigs when we cry too much.

'Why is your life a mistake?' I asked cautiously.

And then Harriet told me the terrible truth. 'I'm the only one in my class who's still a virgin.' She sat down on the airing cupboard floor, howling with the shame of it.

Fifteen. She was fifteen and she had failed the fifteen-plus. When I was fifteen they were still cutting words like 'bum' out of Shakespeare texts, and the word 'condom' hadn't been invented. (The first time I heard it, I thought it meant some sort of eagle.)

'Being a virgin isn't such a terrible thing,' I said, doubtfully.

'Yes it is. There must be something terribly wrong with me. All my friends have Done It.'

I remembered the day at the High School when Judith Littlewick had come in and said she'd Done It the night before behind the Church Hall after Youth Club. 'What was it like?' we had asked, crowding round her excitedly at break. Judith Littlewick had shrugged. 'Comme ci, comme ça,' she had said. We were in the 'O' level French group. 'But I'd sooner have a good game of hockey.' That had filled me with alarm. I hated hockey.

It didn't seem quite the moment to tell the story to Harriet who had calmed down a little now that the dreadful truth was out.

I had wondered, when AIDS first appeared on the horizon, whether virginity might not perhaps become trendy. But all that had become trendy were strawberry-flavoured condoms. 'I could come with you to the Family Planning Clinic,' I said, going hot and cold at the thought of kitting her out with a Dutch cap and a packet of condoms. It was only three years since I'd been kitting her out with sensible shoes for secondary school.

Her eyes filled with tears. 'Oh Mum,' she said. 'Do I have to?'

'No,' I said. 'Of course you don't. And I bet that half the girls who say they have haven't really and are too ashamed to admit it.' Then I told her the story about Judith Littlewick and the Church Hall and the game of hockey, and she laughed and got dressed and went out to buy a hockey stick.

Chapter 11

On Sophie's first day at school, four people said to me, 'I suppose you'll be going back to teaching now.' I caught a bus into Tarminster to practise being by myself. It was unnerving at first, not being on a permanent tilt to clutch Sophie's sticky hand.

I felt depressed, as if I were about to turn up a mental cul-de-sac where I would stay for the rest of my life. I didn't want to go back to the rush between home and work, the divided loyalties, the guilt of leaving a sick child at home, the guilt of staying at home to take care of her while other people covered for me at work.

I went into a café to think. There was an old shopping list in my pocket and on the back of it I wrote: 'Reasons for going back to work' and 'Reasons for not going back'. Under 'Reasons for going back' I put 'Money. At your age you should be aiming for a tumble-dryer and a freezer. Stimulus: You loathe housework.' Under 'Reasons for not going back' I put: 'I don't want to. I want something else.' But I couldn't remember what it was.

'Did you want anything?' the waitress asked crossly.

'I can't remember,' I replied and she stared at me pityingly. 'A cup of tea, please,' I said hurriedly.

I was drinking the tea when the old woman came in. She was enormous and she wore a grey balaclava underneath a black trilby. I'd seen her before, asleep on a bench at

Tarminster station or in the shelter in the Park. Inside her grey trousers, her legs were swollen by old newspapers cross-gartered with binder twine and she was carrying two large plastic bags which she dumped underneath the table next to mine. I smelled her as soon as she sat down. Money and security keep you from smelling like that.

'Cup of tea please, dearie,' she called to the waitress.

'We don't serve drinks without food,' said the waitress in a bored voice. 'You'll have to have a cake.'

'How much for tea and cake?' asked the old woman.

'Ninety pence,' the girl said triumphantly.

'I've only got thirty-five pence.'

'Then you'll have to go, won't you?' snapped the waitress.

The old woman stared at the floor. 'I haven't had a drink since yesterday.'

'Sorry,' said the waitress, who obviously wasn't. 'It's the rule.'

I ordered another cup of tea and when the waitress brought it, I carried it over to the old woman. 'You can't do that!' cried the waitress, 'I brought that tea for you, not her.'

'I paid for it,' I pointed out, 'and I can do what I like with it.'

The old woman grinned at me and winked. 'Thanks, dear,' she said.

The waitress was furious. 'People like her put decent customers off.' And she rushed off to get the manager.

The café doors swung open and a large, noisy family of Canadians swung in. The manager strode out of the wings to have a row with me while my old woman went on drinking her tea and the waitress took the Canadians' order. Steaks, chips, banana splits . . . they stopped talking to listen to the manager telling me to drink up my own tea or get out. I was overtaken by a great swoop of indignation.

How dare this mean-minded little man, or anybody else, tell me what to do? I stood up. As I squeezed past her, the old woman put her hand on my arm. 'That's right, dearie,' she croaked. 'You'll be all right. You do just what you want to and don't let anybody stop you.'

As I pushed through the café doors, I heard the loud Canadians inviting her to join them for a meal. 'Another plate of steak and chips,' they called to the defeated waitress. I felt glad that the whole world wasn't small and mean.

Back home with Sophie, I thought about the morning. 'I want to be in charge of myself,' I said out loud to the fish fingers, 'but I want to be at home.' 'So find something you can do from home,' said the smelly old woman inside my head. I drew a blank. 'Look at me,' said the Baglady. She was so clear inside my head that I found a piece of paper and wrote her down.

Lady of the railway station,
Plastic-bagging queen,
No address, no situation,
Where've you come from?
Where've you been?

Lady looking for your reasons,
Searching through the litter bin,
Other people's times and seasons,
Other people's rhymes and reasons,
Where've they come from?
Who've they been?

'Load of sentimental rubbish,' said the Baglady, jabbing her grimy forefinger at my effort. 'Doesn't scan. And you've put "reasons" twice in the same verse. Still, at least you've done something.'

Chapter 12

On Sophie's second day at school, five people said, 'You won't know what to do with yourself.' 'Oh yes I will,' I said and rode my bicycle very fast and purposefully up and down the village street three times. Then I did the shopping, washed up the breakfast things, rode the bike again, cooked Roger's lunch, washed it up and sat in the garden for an hour and a half until it was time to go back to the school to meet Sophie. It had been a wonderful day.

But on the third day, the guilt began to rise. I shopped and cooked and washed up and bought a local paper to look for a job. You can't go on being relaxed and happy for ever, can you? There I was, at home, and free to read and think and sit in the garden and knit, a shameful kept woman, while Roger slaved on to earn the housekeeping money. I would have to find something sensible to do to justify my existence between half past nine and half past three. I applied to be a postman, but my bicycling wasn't good enough. I nearly applied to be a waitress and washer-up, but I seemed to have spent most of my life doing that.

I whizzed round the village in desperate circles wondering what to do with myself and my life. In the whizzing I met other women in their late thirties and early forties, women like me who had just seen their last children through the school gates and who were dithering on the brink of the next stage in their own lives. All of a sudden I understood why some women go on and on having babies. They want them and need them because the familiar demands that each new baby brings save their mothers the trouble of asking all these tiresome existential questions. It might work for them, but I knew it wouldn't work for me.

I thought about doing another degree, and sent for the Open University syllabus. But in order to pay for that, I'd have to get a job, and if I had a job, I wouldn't have the time or energy for the course.

I climbed aboard my bike again and was held up by groups of terribly nice elderly ladies who were doing good works and who felt that I might be ready to join them. I did try to be good. I joined committees and wrote letters asking for volunteer collectors and raged in my heart and soul against the virtue of it all. After a month of being particularly good, I was desperate for some sin. I telephoned a pre-marriage, passionate and unreal boyfriend one evening, when everyone else was out or in bed. The sound of his voice on the end of the line sent me weak at the knees with lust and sick to the heart with guilt. I'd be no good at adultery. I'd get hopelessly tangled up about loyalty and family life and love and security. So I rang off without even saying who I was. I have watched with admiration all my friends who do it easily; they have affairs without rocking any boats, or they jump out of the boats and live brightly ever after. But I was too much of a coward to take the risk. I had to stay in my boat and row it into a new creek.

And so I had crossed another baby, the Open University, good works and adultery off my list of possible activities. I was getting better at cycling by this time, but the postman job had been given to somebody else. I was also beginning to understand why some women went to the doctor for tranquillizers to dampen down these feelings of guilt and redundancy and restlessness.

Jean and Susie and I talked about it over coffee in Shangri-la one morning. It was easier for them in a way, because farmers' wives can never feel redundant, and Jean had been through most of her mid-life crisis when Kevin gave up being a rising executive to turn into a woodcarver. Even so, they knew what I was talking about. 'The thing I refuse to be,' said Jean, 'is someone who just looks for things to do to fill in the time. It's got to have some meaning to it, some feeling of moving forwards.'

I thought about that for the rest of the day. That was it, of course. That was why an old love affair couldn't work, why anything that I had done twenty years before couldn't work, because they all pulled me back into someone I used to be, instead of taking me forwards into what I might be going to be.

And something in my head said, 'Wait. Just wait. When you can't make up your mind, sit still and don't do anything. And after a while it will become clear and be perfectly obvious which way you should go.'

So I parked my bike and sat still. The phone rang. It was Sophie's teacher. Sophie was running a high temperature and could I go and collect her straight away. She'd got chickenpox.

After she had recovered and gone back to school, the phone rang again. It was a hospital 200 miles away to say that my eighty-year-old aunt had just been brought in with a worn-out heart and was not likely to live for much longer. I caught a train to go and see her and found her being very sensible about the whole thing.

'Look,' she said, 'I'm going to die. There's a letter in the left-hand drawer of my dressing-table labelled "To be opened immediately after my death." Be a dear and go to the flat and get it. Here are the keys.' She passed me the keys to her flat and then fished around in her handbag for something else. 'Take these as well,' she said, holding out a second ring of keys. 'They're for my car. I'd like you to have it.' I couldn't think of anything to say, so I did as I was told and found the letter in the left-hand drawer of the dressing table. I took it back to the hospital. 'Thank you,' said my aunt. 'Open it.'

'But you haven't died yet,' I objected.

'I know,' she said cheerfully, 'but there are one or two things that need to be changed.' The one or two things turned out to be instructions about where to find her papers, her bank statements, her rent book, her will, which were now in the bottom left-hand corner of her wardrobe instead of on the top right-hand shelf. She told me what to cross out and what to write in its place. The rest of the letter was about funeral arrangements and notices for the local paper. You could tell she used to do props and publicity for the Operatic and Dramatic Society. 'You'll need to change the ownership papers for the car,' she pointed out, and told me where to find the registration documents. I found them and we filled them out and signed them together. 'And I'd like you to have power of attorney for me while I'm still alive. It means you can sign my cheques and draw my pension.' I gulped. For the past sixteen years I'd only had power of attorney for my own miserable overdraft. 'Of course you can handle it,' said my aunt firmly, reading my mind, 'it'll be good for you.'

So suddenly I was a woman with a power of attorney and a car, a woman of financial responsibility who could deal with doctors and solicitors and undertakers, a woman who had to get her car insured and earn enough money to run it.

My aunt died easily two days later and I drove back down the motorway and went indoors to meet my family, who had coped very well without me. I felt different. I was a free-range housewife, mistress of my own life between the hours of 9.15 and 3.30 Mondays to Fridays, free to drive through the county in my ancient Andante in search of adventures. I might go potato picking or washing up, I might learn to drive a bus, I might stay at home and read all the books I'd been meaning to read for years or I might learn to cook.

But whatever I did, I'd got a power of attorney and a little white car who may have had the body of a twelve-year-old Andante but who had the heart and stomach of a red MG. Anything could happen.

Chapter 13

Anything could happen. And it did. Dear God and bloody hell, it did. One day I turned around and Roger wasn't there. Not that he was literally not there; his feet and his bones and his skin were there, going to work, coming home, washing up, going out. But his eyes and everything inside him had turned away and were scanning horizons beyond me. I felt very lonely and very frightened, like a small child who has been abandoned in a strange country.

My big sister Mollie, who is tough and efficient and who's got a season ticket to the divorce court, could not understand why I was making such a fuss about something which was happening to practically everybody we knew. She pointed out that it was hardly surprising if Roger was having a midlife crisis after eighteen years of marriage to me. The only surprising thing, she went on, was that he'd put up with me for so long. 'Most men would have got fed up years ago with coming home to an ovenful of papier-mâché puppet heads for supper or with finding sheets of bad poetry all over the bed.' She said other helpful and perceptive things: I ought to have done Domestic Science instead of Philosophy was one of them. I thanked her for her sensitive and supportive response to my misery and she said not at all, she'd always been good at that sort of thing and had just enrolled for an evening class in Counselling at Tarminster Tech. I said I hadn't realised she was interested in local politics and then I went away and wept.

I could feel my home and family life sliding away from me and I couldn't do anything to stop them and I didn't want to lose them. They were mine. They were where I belonged, what I was about, where I was needed. They might have been slow and sticky and stormy, but they were my life and my landscape and my job, and without them I was nothing.

Where could I go? What could I do? Who could I turn to for help?

'"Connect",' said Mollie. 'Go to "Connect". They are the absolute and utter best for getting people together. I've been to them lots of times and I'm thinking of working for them after I've done my Counselling course.'

I couldn't think of anywhere else to go, and so, feeling like a very small animal without feathers or a shell, I made an appointment with 'Connect'.

The waiting room was full of books called *Like Me, Like You* and *The Speaking Body*. I knew those books. I'd dipped into them many a time in the Do-It-Yourself Psychology section of WH Smith's in Tarminster. I knew all about the unconscious messages we transmit when we sit down, stand up, shake hands, scratch our noses, blink our eyes, turn our heads. With all that literature about, I wondered how anybody ever dared to move at all. If you cross your legs when you sit down, you are rejecting intimacy. If you don't, you are inviting it. If you don't look me unblinkingly in the eye when you speak to me, you've got something to hide; if your handshake is damp and flabby, so is your personality.

The 'Connect' receptionist smiled warmly and caringly at me and shook my hand gently but firmly. 'Would you like a tissue?' she asked.

A door opened and a man stuck his large and hairy head

through it. 'Aha,' he said, 'I'm Gordon,' he said, 'do come in.' He shook my hand, gently but firmly, and invited me to sit down. I sat down and crossed my legs. Then I uncrossed them. Then I crossed them again. My nose began to itch.

We sat in a long and tender silence.

'Is there anything you would like to say?' asked Gordon, gazing at me meaningfully through gentle brown eyes. There was. I said it. 'I hear what you are saying,' said Gordon when I stopped. Well, that was a relief, I thought. I'd been saying it for half an hour, so it would have been an awful waste if he hadn't.

What I'd been saying was that my husband was going away from me and that I was terrified and lonely and eaten up by sadness and I didn't know what to do.

My nose itched on, but I fought the desire to scratch it. I pushed my hands into my lap and held them there. I saw Gordon looking at them thoughtfully and I was seized with a longing to leap up, cross my legs, stick my tongue out, thumb my nose and jump backwards round the room. I suppressed it and sat on.

'Is there anything else you want to say?' asked Gordon.

There was. 'How can I get Roger back?'

Gordon leaned forward and put his face rather too close to mine. 'Where has he gone?'

'Away,' I said. And then, suddenly inspired, I added, 'In his feelings.'

Gordon looked thrown, like an actor whose best line has just been stolen by another actor. Then he rearranged his face, withdrew it and locked me into deadly eye contact. 'We can't change him,' he said magnificently, 'but we can change you. Why do you want him back?'

What could I say? I'd been married to Roger for years. He was my home. My anchor. That was a good one. 'He's my anchor,' I said.

Gordon liked it too. 'Why do you need an anchor?'

I was beginning to get the hang of this. 'Because I'm out of control without one.' I paused for a moment and then leaned forward, uncrossing my legs and spreading out my hands. 'The tide's running out and it's taking me with it.'

Gordon liked that very much. He smiled, leaned back in his chair, crossed his corduroy legs and clasped his big white hands behind his hairy head. 'So you see yourself as a boat. What sort of boat?'

What sort of boat? A rowing boat? A racing yacht? 'I think I'm probably an old paddle steamer with broken paddles and a hole in its side.' I wanted to be helpful.

'And no anchor,' said Gordon. There was a pause while we both thought deeply about anchors.

'So what we've got to do,' said Gordon, 'is to help you to repair yourself and become your own anchor.'

'But I want Roger,' I said and burst into tears.

With a practised hand, Gordon offered me a box of tissues and waited while I blotted myself dry.

'Anyway,' I sniffed, 'I don't see how anybody can be a boat and an anchor at the same time. They're two different things. A boat without an anchor floats away and gets wrecked and an anchor without a boat is just a chunk of dead metal.'

But Gordon was unshaken. 'And what about the chain?' There was nothing I could reply to that and we sat in another deep and meaningful silence until my time was up. 'See you next week,' said Gordon in a voice that was soothing and bracing at the same time. 'If you would just make out the cheque to "Connect"...' I wrote the cheque and made an appointment to see him at the same time the following week.

On the way home, waiting for the traffic lights to turn green, I saw Roger coming out of a pub. He was holding hands with a woman and they were laughing and talking and walking close together and they didn't see me.

Chapter 14

'You must try to think of it as a bereavement,' said Gordon.
I tried and failed. Deaths I had lived through had never
filled me with this jealousy and rage and terror. 'I'm going
to ask you a question,' continued Gordon. 'Be totally
honest with yourself. What did you want to do when you
saw them together?'

'I wanted to punch her in the face and kick him in the
balls,' I replied.

Gordon paused, shocked. But soon he was up and
running again. 'So why didn't you?'

'Because I was in the car and the traffic lights turned
green. Tell me what to do,' I begged.

Gordon smiled; it was a professional smile, gentle, warm
and understanding. I watched it move across his face and
crinkle around his eyes and realised that he had smiled it
before at hundreds of distraught men and women and that
he would smile it again at hundreds more.

'No,' he said, in his warm and caring voice, 'I'm not here
to tell you what to do. I'm here to help you get in touch
with your feelings, to help you find out who you really are
and what you really want.'

What I really wanted was to kick Gordon in the balls
too. 'I think I'm probably too much in touch with my
feelings,' I said.

He shook his big head. 'Nobody can be that,' he said.

'Now, try to be completely honest. Is there anything else you want to talk about?'

'Money,' I replied. 'If Roger goes away for good, I won't be able to survive.' Gordon looked pained. 'We're not really here for that sort of thing. What we are here for is to put you in touch with your feelings. Can you make out the cheque to "Connect"?'

Just as I was signing the cheque, there was a knock on Gordon's door. 'Aha,' said Gordon, 'this must be Deirdre.'

'Who is Deirdre?'

'Deirdre is one of our finest, most experienced Counsellors,' said Gordon proudly. 'I have shared your case with her and she is sure that she can help you. Come in, Deirdre, dear.' The door opened and a woman walked through it. Even her walk was caring. She was the woman I had seen coming out of the pub holding hands with Roger.

I suppose that if I had been truly in touch with my feelings I would have blacked both her understanding eyes. As it was, I merely stamped on Gordon's sandalled feet and kicked him, gloriously and appropriately, in his corduroy crotch. 'As you can see, my dear,' and I smiled sweetly at him, 'I'm well and truly in touch with my feelings. Are you hearing me?' I turned and swept out of the room.

Chapter 15

So there I was, forty-five years old, with no job, no love, no money, three daughters, hundreds of puppets, Mistake and a smashed-up life. It was as if a great hole had opened in the universe and I had fallen through it.

'Now's your chance to find out Who You Really Are,' said Mollie who was reading a book on self-assertiveness and self-reliance. But I knew who I was; or at least who I had been. I was a woman who had wanted to be a mother, who had wanted a home and family, who had believed that her home was a refuge, a place of warmth and comfort.

'Come on,' said Mollie briskly, 'now's your chance to make a New Start. Think of all those wonderful women you read about who get a divorce, get on course, recover themselves, discover themselves.' (She was going to evening classes in Creative Writing at Tarminster Tech.) 'Look on this as an Opportunity for Change, as an Opening of Doors, as a Path to New Horizons. Get out there and Go for It.'

But I didn't know what It was.

'Don't be so negative,' said Mollie impatiently. 'Anybody can do anything they really want to do.' Self-doubt has never been a problem for my sister. 'Do your Own Thing, have a fling and . . . and BINGO! You could end up as a . . . as a Sales Executive, a Prime Minister, a Psychotherapist . . . anything you like.'

I sat there, a miserable, exhausted heap. Mollie was right, of course. I ought to seize the moment to pick myself up, brush myself down and start all over again. I ought to be putting on a brave face and shoulder pads and filofaxes and tracking down a career.

But if I wore shoulder pads, they slipped, and I wasn't even sure what a filofax was. I didn't *want* all that. My family had been the centre of my life and without it I was lost and empty. Without it, I didn't feel that I existed at all. What was going to happen to me? What happens to all the women like me?

The President of the Women's Institute came to see me in my emptiness. She is a model citizen, a paragon, a churchwarden, a Good Woman whose husband made off with a Bad Woman while she was organising the Youth Club Drama Festival. 'You think you're quite a nice person till it happens to you, don't you?' she said. 'When Norman was screwing that tart,' (was this the woman who had led the singing of 'Jerusalem' so stirringly for years?) 'I drove to her house one night and I watched until the downstairs lights went off and the bedroom light went on. And when the bedroom light went off, I reached for the rags and the matches and the can of petrol I had brought with me. I still don't know what stopped me lighting the rags and shoving them through her letter box. Upbringing, I suppose. People like us don't commit arson and murder.'

But now I knew why people did. A pit of primitive emotion seethes just beneath the taut skin of our upbringing, and when the taut skin splits, jealousy and anger and fear burst through the surface and cover everything like lava.

I was jealous, incompetent, insolvent and exhausted. I couldn't go supply teaching because every time I opened my mouth to speak, I was sick. My heart raced, my mouth dried up with panic, there was a gaping wound of grief and loneliness inside me and I couldn't sleep. And the more I couldn't sleep, the more incompetent I became and the less able to go out and earn a living.

Mollie became very bracing and lent me encouraging books about Positive Thinking and Inner Strengths. They made me feel worse. I couldn't think positively and I hadn't got any inner strengths.

'Oh, for goodness' sake,' said Mollie, 'stop making such a fuss and grow up. The trouble with you is, you've absolutely no idea of how to stand on your own feet. You've got no self-esteem and no self-reliance.' She was right. She put on her Counselling voice. 'Look inside yourself and tell me what you see.' I looked and saw a dingy dark grey dishcloth. It smelt of washing up and it was being stretched tautly from all four corners so that a hole had appeared in its middle. I described it to Mollie who looked alarmed and made an appointment for me to go and see a psychotherapist she had met on one of her counselling courses.

I enjoyed the sessions with the psychotherapist, whose name was Miranda. They made me feel important and interesting. 'Look inside yourself and tell me what you see,' she said. I told her about the dishcloth and she was shocked. 'Your self-esteem must be appallingly low,' she said. I tried to cheer her up by offering to sew up the hole. She got very interested. 'Do you think it would be appropriate?' she asked, gazing into my eyes. I shrugged and looked away. It seemed a very grand word to use about an imaginary dishcloth, and anyway, when I tried to mend the hole, I couldn't.

Another evening she gave me a cushion and asked if I'd like to punch it. I said I didn't think I would really. It looked perfectly inoffensive and I could see no reason to attack it. 'What would you like to do?' asked Miranda quietly.

I heard myself say, 'I'd like to scream,' and as I said it, the word turned into the thing. I screamed and screamed like Mr Rochester's mad wife, like Lear on the blasted heath, like seven devils cast into the wilderness. I rolled on the floor and drummed my heels, I beat my thighs with my fists and tore my hair, and still I went on screaming. Miranda galloped around, closing windows and drawing curtains. Then I stopped and sobbed, like a toddler after a tantrum.

I got very good at screaming. It was my talent. I screamed at night alone in the car, driving through deep lanes and over high moors. The theory is that it is good to let the anger out, like pus out of a boil. If you don't, the theory goes, the anger turns in upon itself and you and it becomes depression. And so I screamed and screamed. But each scream tore away a scab so that the wound inside me never had a chance to heal. Whenever I was on my own, hoovering or lying awake in the small hours of the night with my brain burning and my heart racing, I would fly to the phone, dial the 'Connect' number and scream abuse at them or their ansaphone. They were appalled and shocked by my inappropriate behaviour, for none of their training in listening skills had covered mad wives whose husbands had run off with one of their connections.

I screamed at Miranda for a month until she decided that I was ready to graduate to Group Therapy.

Chapter 16

'Person Centred Counselling,' announced the poster. 'Find the Child Within.' The Child Within seemed to be hiding in the middle of a circle on the floor. We sat around it, twelve of us, and waited for something to happen. I stared at the floor. The silence went on and on. Then one of the persons raised his head and smiled round the circle. 'Hello,' he said. 'I'm Mel. I suppose you could call me the leader of this group.' He paused. 'But I don't want to be your leader. I want to be your friend. I want us all to work together at ... whatever it is we need to work at together. I want us to grow and to move forward with our feelings. I want us to explore and discover and share.'

He stopped again to let the words sink in. I was trying to pluck up courage to ask if we could explore plumbing and plastering, but he smiled again and began to share more of his thoughts.

'The most important thing to establish,' his voice was wistful, 'is Trust. Unless we trust one another, we can never move on.' He produced a beanbag and asked us to throw it to each other and to give it a name as we caught it. I dropped it and couldn't think of a name. When he thought enough trust had been established, Mel sat down in the circle again and asked us to try to remember each other's beanbag names.

Then it was time to begin the Search for the Child

Within. Mel told us all to close our eyes and to keep them closed no matter what happened. 'No cheating, no squinting. You are blind. All of you. Blind. All of you are blind.' He paused to make quite sure that we had all heard and understood. 'Move around the room with your eyes closed.' His voice was low and hypnotic. 'Sense the presence of the others in the room. Be sensitive to them, listen for them, smell them, but don't bump into them.' I collided with somebody. 'Be sensitive,' said Mel crossly. I squinted through my eyelashes. 'Keep your eyes closed,' said Mel. 'And find a partner. With your eyes closed. Reach out with your hand until you connect with another hand.' Was I the only cheat squinting through lashes? If I was, nobody could possibly know that I was standing very still in a corner with my hands behind my back, could they? 'There are still two people without a partner,' said Mel. Through the bars of my lashes, I could see a small, grey mouse-like shape wandering desperately across the room, its arms stretched out before it. I put out my hands to fend it off and felt them grasped gratefully by two dry paws.

'Get to know that hand,' cooed Mel. 'Relate to it, make it your friend. Get to know its shape and texture. What is it saying to you?' I was paralysed with embarrassment and unable to remove my hands from the eager fondling of the dry paws. 'When you know the hand, when you feel you know it well, let go of it, leave it behind, go off alone again, always with your eyes closed.' Obediently the mousey paws left mine.

Round and round the room we went, sensitive, blind and silent, until Mel said, 'Now find your friend again. Find that hand, recognise it, greet it, hold it, stay with it.' Through the eyelash bars I saw the small grey mouse rushing towards me and I felt its small grey paws clutch mine.

And then Mel said, 'Make a sound. A sound like the touch

of that hand.' I listened in amazement as the others opened their mouths and began to wail and moan and hum and shout. The small grey mouse drew in its breath and let it out in a series of short, harsh rasps.

'Sorry,' I said, 'I've got to go to the loo.' I escaped into the corridor and headed for the door, but Mel was too quick for me.

'Why do you put up such barriers?' he asked. 'Let go. Trust me.' He took my hand and led me back into the room.

The wailing and moaning and humming had reached a cathartic pitch and Mel's disciples lay on the floor in the circle searching for the children within them. At last the noise subsided and the circle sat up, crossed its legs and sobbed its way to silence. Mel smiled at it and asked it to tell itself how it was feeling. It felt wonderful, it said. Released. Exorcised. United. Strengthened. Consoled. Healed. Then it got up and hugged itself. Was there anything else that anybody needed to ask or to say, enquired Mel, reminding the circle that it was a family, a loving, trusting family. The family smiled lovingly and trustingly at itself. 'Anything at all?' urged Mel. Nothing was forbidden, nothing would shock.

I took a deep breath and spoke into the silence. 'How am I going to mend the roof and plaster the cracks and paint the windows and sweep the chimneys and pay the council tax and buy the food and go to work and look after the kids and bleed the radiators and set the time switch and mend the washing machine and stay alive and cope?' The shock waves crackled round the circle. That was not what it was there for. The Child Within had asked its question, but nobody there would answer it.

There was one other question, but I didn't want to ask it in front of all these people. How was I going to live without anyone to love me?

Chapter 17

The supper things squatted, unwashed and slimy, in the sink. Odd mugs and plates and knives and socks and topless jars of Bovite lay around the living room. My hackles rose. It was half past nine in the morning and the only thing that stirred was an inane television presenter who was shrieking and gesticulating and grimacing into my home. The telephone began to ring.

A dozing heap beneath the duvet in front of the telly heaved and reared up and turned into Jane. 'It's all right Mum, I'll get it. It's bound to be for me.' Bound to be, I thought. I tried not to listen, but intense words and phrases about relationships and subtexts kept breaking through the idiot presenter's squawks. My daughters spoke a different language from the one I used, in what, as they had once kindly explained to me, is the non-specific dialect of their age. It abolishes all consonants and runs together all remaining sounds into a singsong, upturned with a question mark at the end of each phrase. Its beauty, I was told, lies in the fact that it is completely free of any class or educational connotations. Its disadvantage, I once dared to say, is that it is also completely free of sense, logic and communication. Harriet and Jane retorted that a remark like that was a perfect example of my social and educational arrogance.

'Yeah, yeah, yeah,' Jane was saying down the phone, just

like the Beatles. 'Yeah. I dunno. Jowamean?'*

I switched on the hoover and pushed it angrily around the floor between the socks and plates and knives and topless jars. Mistake yapped when the postman shoved the letters through the door. I switched off the hoover and fell over her on the way to pick them up. 'Yeah, yeah, yeah,' said Jane again. 'It's the hidden agenda you've got to watch out for, jowamean?' Shag the hidden agenda, I thought, what about the washing up? I picked up the post. Electricity bill, house insurance reminder, television licence reminder, poll tax demand, telephone bill. Telephone bill. I stared at it, frozen into disbelief. One hundred and seventy-one pounds forty-three pence. It was impossible, it was a mistake. Mistake wagged her tail and looked adoringly at me, and I lashed out at her. According to this phone bill, towns and cities all over the country were linked by soundwaves all leading to my home. 'Yeah, yeah,' said Jane again. It was not a mistake, it was one hundred and seventy-one pounds forty-three pence worth of non-specific dialect conversations about subtexts and hidden agendas.

I spun round and seized the telephone from Jane's astonished hand. 'Enough,' I said.

She gazed at me in appalled disbelief. 'What the hell are you doing?'

'I'm banning the telephone. You and your classless subtextual friends will have to communicate by pigeon from now on.'

Jane was pale with outrage. 'How dare you interrupt my private phone calls?'

I held out the phone bill in a shaking hand. 'This is how I dare. This is how. Who the bloody hell is going to pay for this lot? Have you got a hundred and seventy-one pounds

* 'Jowamean?' is non-specific dialect for, 'Do you know what I mean?'

61

forty-three pence to spare? Because I certainly haven't.'

Jane began to laugh in a superior, spiritual sort of way. 'For God's sake, Mum, it's only money. Life's about more than money, you know. Property is theft, jowamean?'

That did it. Years of trying to be nice to my children, of believing that if I loved them, if I treated them with courtesy and respect and kindness and generosity they would do the same for me, exploded in my face and I spanked Jane hard on her bottom. It was the first time in either of our lives that I had done it.

Her mouth fell open. 'You can't do that.'

I did it again, just to make sure. 'Now you listen to me for once,' I said. 'Just you sit down and listen to me.' There was no subtext here, just one furious woman and a telephone bill.

'Listen to me,' I said again. 'Our generation brought you lot up on a lot of child-rearing theories about the awful dangers of making you constipated and homosexual and depressed and repressed if we ever punished you or criticised you or in any way let you think that you were less than wonderful or deserved anything less than pure happiness. We praised your every word and action, we discussed politics and religion with you before we sat you on your potties, we never made you do anything you didn't want to do and we've reared a whole generation of arrogant spoiled brats with ludicrously inflated ideas about their own talents and importance who are utterly selfish, who shout about Third World human rights while they treat their own mothers like slaves and idiots. Well, this slave and idiot has had enough.' I slammed out of the house and caught the bus to Tarminster, where I realised two things. One was that Jane had been taking the phone call and not making it. The other was that I was still wearing my apron.

When I returned, I could hear Harriet talking on the far

side of the front door. She was on the phone, describing my revolution to a friend. 'Of course,' she was saying, 'I could read her subtext clearly, jowamean? It's redirected anger. Yeah. Like overspill. Right. I mean it wasn't about the phone bill at all really, it was something far deeper than that, jowamean?'

I gritted my teeth, opened the front door and pushed past her into the kitchen. The pile of washing up was deeper than ever.

Chapter 18

The bills came on and on and turned red. I telephoned Glenda (the Duck) Dawson and asked her to give me some supply work. Fortunately, the Personal, Social and Moral Education teacher was away with existential despair and Glenda said that I could stand in for him until he had rediscovered the meaning of the universe. I told her that I was a maniac who drove through the night screaming at the moon and she said, 'So what? The same could be said for most of the teachers here.' I watched the classes through a window of despair, read chapters out of textbooks on Interpersonal Relationships and even had to sit through a lecture by a 'Connect' representative. I set them Personal, Social and Moral Education essays about life being a road and the Ten Commandments being traffic lights, filled in the claim forms and took the money.

And then a day came when I could not get out of bed. The dragging wound in the pit of my stomach held me, rocking with fear and unable to move. Eventually I wrenched myself up and rang Glenda to say I'd got flu. You don't say, 'I'm not coming in today because I'm in a state of cosmic distress and nothing makes sense and there's no point in doing anything because anything you do is only a temporary distraction to take you away from the truth that life and the universe are meaningless, and nobody loves you.' You say you've got flu.

I went back to bed and Mollie came to see me. She lent me a book called *How to Have a Nervous Breakdown Without Pills*. Chapter One was called 'Racing Heart, Dry Mouth and Churning Stomach', Chapter Two was called 'Sweating, Nausea and Giddiness', and Chapter Three was called 'The Tight Cheese Wire Round Your Head'. I found it absolutely gripping because it described in minute and accurate detail every symptom I was getting and several more that I probably would get. It was so convincing that I began to develop the new symptoms as soon as I read about them. I lost my appetite and weight and all interest in anything except my symptoms. 'But don't worry,' said the book. 'This is all perfectly normal. Lie back and relax. Tell your body that it is only experiencing exaggerated fear, that it can't fool you into a heart attack or a stroke.' I wished devoutly that it could. However, I spoke sternly to it. 'You can't fool me,' I said. 'This is only a nervous breakdown. There's nothing really the matter with you.' The great gaping pit opened still wider in my stomach. It was full of sadness and despair and loneliness. 'This is quite normal,' said the book. 'Lie back, relax and drift.' I did as I was told and read the next bit of the book. 'Keep active,' it said. 'Do all the things you enjoy doing.' I didn't enjoy doing anything. I lay in bed and the terror and loneliness and the terrible sense of being abandoned possessed me and the tight wire gripped my scalp and bore like a hot wire through the middle of my forehead. I looked it up in the book. 'This is quite normal,' it assured me.

'Sometimes,' it went on, 'the sufferer becomes so exhausted by anxiety and grief and guilt that he collapses.' I collapsed. 'But don't worry,' said the book, 'the only way from here is up.' I dragged myself up and crawled, heart racing, mouth dry, face sweating, cheese wire tightening, into the kitchen. 'Bugger you,' I said to my body, 'I'll beat you. I'll eat something.' With shaking hands I spread some margarine across a slice of dry brown bread and forced it into my mouth. I bit down on it and one of my front teeth broke off and fell on to the kitchen floor. The book was wrong. There was another way from here. It was down.

I was sitting on the kitchen floor, staring at the broken-off tooth in my hand when Jane walked in.

'Christ,' she said, 'I can't stand any more of this. I'm going.' She stood there looking at me. This was her mother sitting on the floor, unable to move, unable to help her, waiting to be rescued. 'I'm going,' said Jane again. 'I'm going to live with Chas.' My tight mind skidded over Chas. He spent his days playing a guitar and a penny whistle on Cathedral Green surrounded by large dogs and admiring 'A' level students from Tarminster Tech, and his nights in a squat behind the prison. His parents lived in a big house on the Riverside Road. 'Christ,' said Jane again and I could hear the tears in her voice. I tried to say 'Don't go,' but the words wouldn't come. Jane went.

Harriet came in from school. 'What's the matter with you?' She sounded frightened. 'Mum? Why are you sitting on the floor?'

This time I heard my voice coming from a long way off. 'I think I'm ill. I think I want to go into hospital.'

'What d'you mean, ill? What sort of ill? Where's Sophie?' I didn't know. Harriet nudged me with her toe. 'Get up, Mum.' Then she began to scream at me with all the rage and terror and helplessness of months pouring out of her. 'Get up, you stupid cow, get up, get up, get up.'

'I think I want to go into hospital,' I said again.

Harriet's face came in close, twisted with fear. 'Yes, you do that. You bloody do that. You're sick, aren't you? You're round the sodding bend, aren't you? Go on, you go, you go to sodding hospital.'

Chapter 19

The doctor listened to my heart and took my blood pressure. I prayed that he would find me some wonderful real disease like cancer or angina or liver fluke. You can be brave and noble about those and you can stay in bed and fight them while everyone admires your courage and your spirit. But depression, madness, nervous breakdowns are different. They show weakness, moral flabbiness, inadequacy of personality. So I prayed for cancer and AIDS and varicose veins and flu, but no, the doctor said my body was all right. It was my head and my mind and my soul which were wrong.

'We'll keep you in for a few days,' said the doctor.

'I don't think that's a good idea,' I told him.

'Give it a try,' he replied. 'It'll give you time to rest and think.'

I tried to explain that I couldn't rest because I couldn't stop thinking and that thinking was a hideous record which played the same remorseless song over and over again in my exhausted brain. 'You're no good,' it scratched and croaked. 'You never have been any good. You can't do anything. You never could do anything.'

'If you come in here for a bit of a rest,' interrupted the doctor, 'you can talk this through with us. You need to talk this through.'

I pointed out that I had been talking and screaming it

through for months and that now it was time to stop talking and thinking and start doing, otherwise my children and I would be homeless because I was incapable of taking care of us. I went on to tell him that all the talking and thinking and feeling had done was to plough a deep, dark, bleeding pit of sadness in my guts and I'd fallen into it and I couldn't get out. As soon as I heard myself saying it, I knew that I'd made a mistake. I recognised the tremor of excitement running through the doctor and I cursed my tongue. 'Ignore my metaphors,' I told him, 'I'm good at metaphors. What I'm bad at is practical survival.'

But it was too late. He leapt joyfully into the pit. 'If we talk,' he said, 'I'm sure that we can cut some steps up the side of your pit and you will be able to climb out.'

I crossed my legs and scratched my nose. 'How long will this step-cutting take?' I asked.

'Who knows?' said the doctor.

'Listen very carefully,' I said. 'I have no money. I have no job and I'm incapable of getting one because there's an incessant record going round and round in my head telling me that I'm no good at anything, and it's right.'

'That's what we call "negative dialogue",' said the doctor proudly. 'Why don't you write it down?'

I tried to be patient with him. 'I don't want to write it down, I want to forget it.'

'I still think you need a rest,' said the doctor.

And he was right. Away from home, away from all responsibility, safe in a numb limbo, in a time-warp where nobody expected anything from me, where other people cooked my food, made my decisions, left me alone, the record in my head slowed down and stopped and I began to sleep again.

Chapter 20

It was dinner time in the psychiatric annexe of Tarminster General. I followed the smell of lasagne and custard along the corridor and joined the queue leading to a huge metal trolley. It was just like being in the dinner queue at the High School in the fifties (except that lasagne had not then arrived in England). I found a seat at a table and sat down next to a massive and broken-nosed young man with a cauliflower ear. He glared at me without speaking and we ate in complete silence.

The silence was broken by a yell from the corridor, and a thin, pale, pretty girl hurtled into the dining room. 'No, I sodding won't eat your sodding dinner, you sodding cow,' she shrieked, spinning round to face a placid, motherly woman who was shepherding her towards the food trolley.

The woman shrugged. 'Please yourself. But you know you get evil-tempered when you don't eat.' The girl, who was about twenty, sat on the floor and lit a cigarette. 'Come on Shirley, you know you can't smoke in the dining room. It's not fair on the others. Get up.' Shirley, who was dressed in skin-tight leggings and a lot of lipstick, curled up in a ball on the floor, puffed on her cigarette and blew smoke at the woman who sighed, put an arm round her and spoke firmly. 'We, you and I, are going out of this room right now,' she said. 'I will not allow you to blow smoke over everybody else's food, so get up and bugger off.'

Shirley uncurled herself, got up, swore and buggered off.

I finished my dinner and picked up my plate to take it to the slop bucket. As I scooped bits of left-over lasagne into the bucket and tipped my knife and fork into the plastic bowl of water next to it, I remembered school again and the days and weeks and terms of ladling scraps into the pig bucket under the outraged eye of the Maths mistress, who could not countenance wasted food and who we almost feared would make us eat up those mushy remains from the pig bucket itself. Before we ate our meals, she would stand angrily on the stage and snap: 'For what we are about to receive may the Lord make us truly thankful for Christ's sake sit down.' My memory meandered back to the RI mistress whose graces went on for so long and with such devout conviction that there was hardly any time left to eat what we were supposed to be so truly thankful for. I remembered the day that she asked Judith Littlewick, whose sexual life was legendary in 4A, why she was wearing seven small plastic clothespegs clipped to the lapel of her school blazer. Quick as a flash, Judith had replied that they were there to help her remember the Seven Deadly Sins. The RI mistress had been enchanted. 'Ah,' she had twittered excitedly, 'I see. Each colour represents a different sin. What a clever idea, Judith.' We had laughed until we ached. I hoped now that poor innocent Miss Goodenough had never found out the real symbolism of those clothespegs. They were a scoring system for our sexual adventurousness and they went from one to ten. One meant a closed-mouth kiss, two meant a French kiss and so on up to ten. Most of us never got past four, even when we were in the sixth form and too sophisticated to wear the clothespegs, but Judith Littlewick was wearing ten before the end of 'O' level.

'Excuse me,' said a voice beside me and I jumped back into the present. It was Broken Cauliflower who was trying to get past me to the slop bucket. I moved out of his way quickly.

'Sorry,' I said. He was not the sort of man I wanted to offend. But he was so surprised at not being told to shag off that he invited me to join him in a game of Scrabble. I thanked him effusively and followed him to the Scrabble box.

We had just picked out our opening seven letters when Shirley slunk over to the table. 'Can I play, Brian?' she asked, pouting at Broken Cauliflower.

'Nope,' he replied.

'Why not, you bastard?'

'Because you can't spell.'

She picked up his shelfful of letters and tipped them on to the floor smiling sweetly at him as she did so. 'At least,' she murmured tenderly into his cauliflower ear, 'at least I'm not a sodding paranoid schizophrenic.'

He stood up and picked her up in a fireman's lift. 'And at least I'm not a selfish spoilt brat. And at least I can spell paranoid schizophrenic.' He carried her across the room and dumped her on a sofa, and then he returned to the board where I had picked up his letters and put them back on to his shelf.

'That's no use, is it?' he said. 'You've seen what I've got now.' I swore I hadn't. 'On your mother's grave?' he asked.

'She's not dead yet.'

We both laughed and then he beat me soundly. At the end of the game, after he had added up the scores, he glowered at me. 'Don't ever patronise me,' he warned, and I never did. I never beat him at Scrabble either.

Brian and I got to know each other. He'd worked on and off building sites ever since he'd left school ten years before, without qualifications or ambitions or hope. He was frequently consumed with rage at the impossibility of

71

understanding the point of existence; he was also immensely kind.

But I never got to know the young man with the sweet smile and the Ph.D in genetic engineering who apologised to everything he ate before he ate it, but found it quite impossible to talk to anybody else.

I made friends with the wildly creative and zingingly attractive Nick who played the guitar to release his pent-up power, painted staggering pictures, wrote high-flying poetry and could find no sensible way of earning a living so had ended up homeless, frequently drunk and asleep on pavements, waking up to hate himself and the world.

In the bedroom next to mine was Marjorie, who wept inconsolably for the husband who had died without warning one night three months before. 'He was so cold,' she kept saying. 'I just reached out my hand to touch him and he was so cold and I couldn't wake him up.'

There was a man called Mike whose wife had told him that he was ugly, useless, no good in bed, no good anywhere. Then she had left him, taken their child and gone to live with a rock drummer. He had believed what she had said, proved that she was right by losing his job, climbed into a hot bath and slit his wrists. A neighbour had noticed red water running into the drain they shared and had climbed in through the bathroom window in time to staunch the blood and get him into hospital.

'Life,' said Brian, 'is like a fruit machine. It's just a matter of chance which way your genetic recipe falls: two lemons and a raspberry; a banana, a pineapple and a plum; three apples. After that it's a question of what comes along to bash you or cuddle you.'

'Oh shut up,' I said as I tried again to beat him at Scrabble, read Nick's tempestuous poetry with awe and emptied the slops into the waste bin.

Chapter 21

Two weeks later I went home. I just caught the bus back to Honeyford and went home. Mistake looked up from under reproachful lids, wagged the end of her tail doubtfully, but wouldn't get up to greet me. My heart sank. Was this how it was going to be? Did I look wrong, smell wrong? Would dogs and toddlers be afraid of me, would school queue mothers blush and look away when they saw me coming? Would the people behind the counters greet me with the false jollity they reserved for the very old, the very young and the very inadequate?

I looked at the clock. Five to three. I could, if I dared, go to meet Sophie from school. I drew a deep breath, put the choke-chain on Mistake and dragged her through the front door. I would go via the Post Office to collect the back numbers of the Family Allowance. I remembered the day when I had risked it all on a horse called Teapot and spent the winnings on Shangri-la. 'You do what you want to do, my duck,' the Baglady had said. I had. And look where it had got me.

Still, the record that had scratched around my brain for so long had stopped. I stepped out into the street and Mistake yapped and tugged at the chain. Nola Gleeson was wobbling along towards me. 'Hello, love,' she said. 'Haven't seen you about for a while. Been away?'

'I've been on holiday.'

'Good for you,' said Nola. 'Had a good time?'

'Yes, lovely, thank you.' I turned and bolted back into the house, dragging Mistake behind me. No, I couldn't face the village. Not yet.

Then the phone rang and it was Sophie's best friend Charley's mother. 'Thank goodness I've caught you,' she said. 'I've got a crisis. The baby's come out in a rash and I've got to take him to the surgery. Could you get Charley from school and bring her back to you for an hour or so, till I can get her?'

I said of course I could, and then I stopped. Would she want to leave Charley with me if she knew? I hesitated, plucked up the courage and said, 'I've just spent two weeks in hospital being treated for depression. Is that all right?'

There was the briefest of pauses. Then, 'Of course it's all right. Don't be so silly,' said Charley's mother. I wonder if she had any idea of what she'd done.

I rang Mollie, said that I would pick up Sophie, then grabbed Mistake's lead again and braved the village. Mothers were everywhere, gossiping, grumbling, confiding, with babies and buggies and toddlers and dogs and plastic bags banging and tangling around their legs. I looked at them all, tied up in their safety, confident of their identities, sure of who they were and why they were and what they were doing. They belonged with the husbands they grumbled about, with their freezers and their microwave ovens and their broken nights and their wonderful security. And I wondered if any of them ever stopped and thought about what would happen when the babies were out of the buggies and the children were out of the schools and they found themselves face to face with husbands who didn't want them any more.

Sophie flung herself at my knees. 'Hello,' she said, 'had a nice holiday? Where's Mollie?'

'She's not coming. You'll have to put up with me.'

'OK. Can Charley come and play?'

'Hello,' said the Family Allowance lady behind the Post Office counter, 'have you had a nice holiday?'

'Yes thank you, very nice,' I said.

On the way home, Nola Gleeson overtook me, earrings jangling, high heels clacking on the pavement. 'Nola,' I said, 'I haven't been on holiday. I've been in hospital being treated for depression.'

Nola grinned. 'Happens all the time.'

'Does it really?'

'Course it does. Too much strain, too much worry, not enough money, not enough love and poof! Look at me.' I looked at her, brave in her high heels and make-up and cheap jewels, carrying her bottle of vodka home from the off-licence on pension day, living on Social Security in her bedsitter with her poodle and her budgie, clanking bawdily and gaudily and courageously through her life. 'Life's a bugger, but you've just got to take it by the throat and show it who's master. Tell you what, you need a bit of fun after that place. Come out with me to Bingo, Monday night.'

Chapter 22

Huge men with hairy golden skin and tattooed biceps bulged through pink and turquoise vests across the pool table. Dainty men with pointed noses and close-set eyes flicked treble twenties disdainfully at the dart board. A woman with an awesome figure squashed into a tight black leather skirt and a tighter pink embroidered jumper propped half her bottom on a bar stool and gazed challengingly around the room. Women I had never met but whom I recognised from the Post Office on pension day edged their way between the tables, clutching their Bingo books, tight-haired and grim-faced with determined expectation. 'It's like a religion for some of them,' said Nola Gleeson scornfully. I followed her through the maze of tables to the top of the bar where the Bingo books were being sold.

'Can I see your membership card?' said the Bingo man to me.

'This lady is here as my guest,' said Nola with dignity. That put him in his place and he sold me a book for a pound.

I followed Nola back between the tables to the bottom end of the bar and sipped at the vodka she bought me.

'All right Nola?' asked the leather skirt.

Nola pretended not to hear and began to explain the mysteries of Bingo to me. 'You start this way up till you get to the end then you turn over and come back the other way.'

The leather skirt screamed with laughter. 'And if anybody knows how to turn over and come back the other way, it's old Nola. Isn't that right, Nola?'

Nola rose with superb calm and led the way from the bar to a table in the far corner of the Institute. 'There's a certain class of person who ought never to be allowed in here,' she said, and then we got down to the business of the evening. 'It's not just a simple house. Sometimes he'll start off with a line or pyramid or end numbers.' I was lost already, but Nola was a patient teacher and after a minute or two I grasped that a line of numbers crossed off was a line, that one on the top line, two on the second and three on the third was a pyramid and that end numbers just meant end numbers.

A tide of women flowed through the Institute doors and the pool players and the dainty dartsmen ebbed and disappeared until the room was full of serious Bingoists. A silence settled over us.

'Good evening, Ladies and Gentlemen and welcome,' said the Bingo Master over a loudspeaker. 'And just to start the brain cells ticking over, we'll go for end numbers first.' Nola was busily underlining all her end numbers and I followed suit.

'Four and Two, Forty-Two; Seven and Eight, Seventy-Eight; on its own, Number Three; all the Twos, Twenty-Two; Legs Eleven; Top of the Board, Number Ninety; Five and Three, Fifty-Three . . .' Nola's biro was making furious crosses all over her page but I couldn't keep up with the calls. 'All the Eights, Eighty-Eight.'

'Two fat ladies,' I said quietly.

'Shush.' Nola was shocked. 'You aren't allowed to say that any more, it's offensive.'

'Blind Forty, Four O,' said the Bingo Master and 'Yes' came a voice from somewhere up the room and the first game was over.

In the interval that followed while the Bingo Master checked the winning numbers against his computer, Nola explained how the book was arranged in columns. 'Single numbers down the left, tens in the next column, twenties in the next and so on to the eighties with ninety at the top of the board.' This was an invaluable piece of information. Now all I had to do was to run my eye up and down the columns and cross off the numbers as the Bingo Master called them. Knowing about the columns changed everything. Now I was on course for a full house.

'Number One, Kelly's Eye; on its own, Number Six; Three and Four, Thirty-Four; top of the board, Number Ninety.' Nola nudged me and pointed to the middle block of my page. 'Only two to go.' 'Two and Eight, Twenty-Eight; Seven and Six, Seventy-Six.' I crossed off the seventy-six and waited breathlessly, my biro poised above the one remaining number in the middle block. It was sixty-five. 'All the Twos, Twenty-Two; Four and Eight, Forty-Eight; Six and Five, Sixty-Five.'

'Sixty-five,' I yelped, scarlet with embarrassment. The game halted.

'Did I hear House?' enquired the Bingo Master.

'Over here,' said Nola and shoved me to my feet. 'Go on, take it up.'

The Bingo Master and his sidekick checked my crossed-off numbers against their computer, agreed that I had indeed achieved a full house and handed me five pounds. Blushing with triumph now, I wove my way back to Nola who was beaming proudly at me. It was like the one and only time I had received the school prize for Effort in Deportment at the High School Speech Day.

We were off again, looking for a pyramid this time. The leather skirt got there first, to Nola's obvious disgust, and then it was down to the serious business of a full house. Again I was waiting for two numbers, again one of them was called, again I hung like a hawk over my last number, again it was called. Another five pounds richer I returned to Nola and settled down for an endgame.

I won that as well. I bought Nola two more vodkas to thank her for her tuition and we trod an unsteady path home from the Institute. 'See?' said Nola, 'you're a bleeding winner after all. Nobody's ever won three games like that on the trot in all the years that I've been coming. Somebody up there must be keeping an eye on you.' She hiccupped and tripped. 'God Moves in a Mysterious Way,' she giggled. He certainly does, I thought, rolling my winnings around in my pocket.

When I got home, Jane was in the kitchen. 'Hello, Mum,' she said. 'I've come back.'

Chapter 23

Charley's mother hadn't minded. Nola Gleeson hadn't minded. Jane had come home. I had won thirteen pounds at Bingo and I wasn't a bleeding loser after all. And then Susie Jenkins' sister Kate, who is a famous salmon fisherwoman on our river, rang up and asked me if I would like to go out poaching. 'We've got an all-women's crew this year,' she explained, 'but Mary's just gone into labour, so we're one short.' Mary is their other sister. I accepted. Kate and Susie's family has been poaching the river for generations and it was a huge honour to be invited to join them. 'Meet me and Auntie on the causeway at one o'clock tomorrow morning. Susie's got some waders you can borrow. Keep your mouth shut, mind.'

I told Harriet and Jane that I'd been invited to a party, which was loosely true, and they agreed to Sophie-sit. I collected the waders from Susie and practised walking round the garden in them when nobody was looking. They flapped around my thighs and I had to attach them to myself with bits of string which were tied to another bit of string around my waist.

At half past midnight, the boots and I plodded down the causeway. The night was dark and the tide was low. A small wind began to blow up the river and I felt lost and lonely. I walked down to the end of the causeway, turned and walked back to the Riverside Road to wait for Kate and Auntie.

The Riverside Road is grand and wealthy and the people who live there give dinner parties. As I stood underneath a street lamp on a corner in my anorak and thigh boots, a house on the opposite corner began to disgorge its guests. I could hear voices I recognised shouting effusive thanks and lips smacking against cheeks as diners wobbled into their cars, started their engines and drove towards me. Headlights shone into my eyes, a window slid open and a head poked out and stared at me. It was Mollie's. I stepped quickly out of the lamplight and pulled my collar up around my ears.

A beaten-up Cortina braked beside me and Kate jumped out. 'All ready then?'

Auntie arrived on a bicycle which she rode straight past us without speaking and disappeared. Five minutes later, she re-appeared on foot. Kate handed me a pair of oars and led the way down the causeway and into the mud.

Auntie fished a pipe out of her pocket, stuffed it with tobacco and lit it. 'Wash your boots off before you get into the boat,' she growled. I did as I was told. I sat at the back of the boat, Auntie sat in the front smoking her pipe and Kate rowed in the middle. 'We'll shoot the Maiden first,' she said. Auntie grunted.

Silently we slipped away down the river. The moon slid out from behind a cloud and the mudbanks gleamed silver on either side of us. I looked back to the Riverside Road; the street lamps had gone out and everything was in darkness there now. Kate rowed strongly and Auntie sat silently, sucking on her pipe.

'Right,' said Kate, a quarter of an hour later. 'This is the Maiden.' A stretch of shingle glinted in the moonlight. 'It's a good hole for a beginner to shoot because the ground's hard. You won't sink in the mud here. You two get out. Stay close behind Auntie in case you fall down a hole.' Auntie stepped out over the side of the boat and I scrambled after her, landing up to my thighs in the river. She held a three foot long wooden pole in her arms. She dropped it in the water and walked away across the Maiden, holding a length of rope which was tied to the pole.

'Can I help at all?' I asked.

'No,' said Auntie. So I didn't.

'See you later,' called Kate from the boat, and she rowed away out into the middle of the river. I could see her in the moonlight, paying out the net over the stern of the boat. Then she turned upstream and rowed ahead of us.

'Come on,' snarled Auntie and I followed her along the edge of the Maiden. The wooden pole bobbed along on the tide beside her like a pet fish on a lead.

Kate rowed on and then turned back towards the Maiden and landed a hundred yards upstream of us. Auntie and the pole and I continued our slow and silent walk towards her. The corks on the top of the net ballooned and bobbed out into the river. Kate was out of the boat and pulling in the end of the net and Auntie was doing the same with our end. They moved towards each other, hauling slowly and rhythmically, hand over hand, leaning back against the tide and the moonlight. Something leapt and then another thing and then another, thrashing and racing in the curve of the net. The women stood together hauling in the net and crouching low. 'They're in the bunt,' grunted Auntie, 'watch they don't slip out.'

The women pulled and pulled. The fish rolled over and struggled in the net, Kate and Auntie untangled them and put them in the bottom of the boat. Then they coiled the net back into the boat and Auntie rowed upriver for the second shoot. 'You stay with me this time,' said Kate, and handed me the oars. Auntie and the pipe and the pole went ashore on to a stretch of mud called the Old Whore. 'She's tricky to walk if you don't know her,' Kate explained. I rowed across the river, then turned upstream with the net trickling out over the back of the boat. 'Take it as slow as you possibly can,' said Kate. 'It's not actually illegal unless you stop completely.' We turned back in towards the shore where Auntie and the pole were squelching and bobbing with the tide, and I saw another salmon leap inside the half-moon of the net. We caught four more on that shoot. 'Time to go home,' said Kate. 'I want to see if Mary's had her baby yet.'

They hauled the net back into the boat again, then Kate took the oars and rowed up with the tide. Halfway to the causeway, Auntie sniffed and pointed. Lights were shining from an attic window in one of the houses on the Riverside Road. 'Bugger,' said Kate. 'That's Lady Hennessey's signal.' She changed direction and rowed back down against the tide. 'Water bailiffs are about,' she whispered. 'Lady Hennessey always switches on that light to warn us.'

'What are you going to do?' I asked.

'Wait and see,' said Kate.

The moon had gone behind another cloud and it was safely dark. Kate rowed us in against a wall where the water lapped against a hole. Auntie was busy with old sacks and sweaters in the bottom of the boat, wrapping four of the fish carefully in them and tying them up firmly. 'OK,' she said to Kate.

'This is where we need you,' Kate said to me. 'Go ashore now. You'll find Auntie's bike parked up against the wall. Get it and ride like mad across the field to the Trickle. The bailiffs don't know about you, but they know us and they'll be suspicious if we aren't both in the boat when we land at the causeway. So you bike to the Trickle. There are three big oaks on the bank and right below the middle one you'll see the other end of the drain. It's like a postbox. Anything we put in this end shoots through and comes out there. It takes about twenty minutes to wash through, which gives you plenty of time. You've got to bike to the other hole and pick up the fish when they float through. There's a basket on the bike, you'll be all right. Take the fish back to your house and I'll pick 'em up as soon as the coast's clear.'

I climbed over the side of the boat, waded ashore and found the bike. 'Right,' whispered Auntie and posted the sweaterfuls of salmon into the drain. I wobbled up into the big field that separates the Flood from the Trickle; it wasn't easy to cycle in waders, but I got there in time. Down the slope to the three big oaks, and under the middle one I found the hole with the tide half way up it. I crouched above it, waiting. And then they came, all four of them at once, into my arms and into the basket over the handlebars. I pushed home, shaking and exhausted, parked the salmon in the sink and fell asleep, still wearing the waders.

The phone woke me. 'Good morning, my dear,' boomed Lady Hennessey aristocratically. 'I wondered whether you would like to come to dinner tonight? Nothing formal. Only a few close friends.'

Chapter 24

Mollie was among the few close friends. She entered Lady Hennessey's house with her usual panache and a small man in her wake. 'This is Dick,' she announced proudly. 'He's my new Relationship,' she added to me in a whisper. 'He's a New Man.' I couldn't help thinking that he looked rather old as he stood obediently in Mollie's lee, wearing open-toed sandals and a mild expression. Lady Hennessey sat me next to Dick at the dinner table. The other close friends were the President of the Women's Institute and the Water Bailiff and his wife. The Water Bailiff sat on my other side and Mollie sat opposite Dick, making a lot of eye contact with him. I tried to think of something to say.

'Have you and Mollie known each other long?' I asked cautiously, in case he was listening for hidden agendas or checking out my body language.

The Relationship blushed. 'We met on an Aromatherapy course,' he murmured, 'then we both went to Massage and now we've bumped into each other in Counselling.'

'Gosh,' I said.

Then Mollie locked him into eye contact again. 'I thought that last lecture on Interfacing was riveting, didn't you?' she said.

I was confused. Did they do dressmaking as well on these courses?

'Riveting,' agreed Dick obediently. 'It's a concept I hadn't explored before.'

'Do you do it all by hand?' I asked politely, 'or do they provide machines?' Dick and Mollie stared at me. The Water Bailiff's wife was trying not to giggle. 'For the interfacing,' I explained. The awful silence that followed was broken by choking noises from the Water Bailiff's wife. To cover up, I asked Dick where he worked and he replied that he was a freelance aromatherapist and masseur and soon he would be a freelance counsellor as well. I looked at him, all small and pale and gentle in his sandals and I was washed by a sudden wicked longing for wild strong men who slew dragons, swept women on to white horses and made passionate love to them on mountaintops.

Mollie kicked me viciously under the table. 'You simply have no conception of the beauty of non-sexual relationships, have you?' she spat. I was completely bewildered.

'I didn't know we were talking about relationships. I thought you'd been on a dressmaking course,' I said. 'Interfacing was one of those awful things we had to do in needlework at school. You know, when you sew strips of stiff white stuff inside collars to make them lie flat.'

Mollie was not amused. 'It's a term we use about the development of inter-personal relationships,' she hissed. Then she smiled like a shark and raised her voice. 'I'm sure I saw you under the street lamp near the causeway at about one o'clock this morning,' she said, with sweet fascination. 'You were wearing leather thigh boots. What on earth were you doing?'

'Don't be ridiculous,' I replied, 'I haven't got any leather thigh boots.' I turned to the Water Bailiff. 'Your job must be frightfully interesting,' I said.

'Oh it is,' he replied. Lady Hennessey's companion served the main course. It was poached salmon.

After dinner, over coffee and brandy in the drawing

room, the conversation turned to domestic help and the difficulty the Water Bailiff's wife was having in finding somebody to help her clean her house. I was sitting next to her on the sofa. 'I'll do it,' I heard myself say, and sipped at my third glass of brandy.

'Don't be ridiculous,' snapped Mollie, 'You're hopeless at housework. Anyway, you've got a degree in Philosophy.' I saw my sister very clearly through the alcohol.

'Third class,' I said. 'Stop telling me what I'm hopeless at and go and find Dick. He's probably massaging somebody into a trusting relationship in the kitchen.' I turned back to the Water Bailiff's wife.

Chapter 25

The Water Bailiff's household was a joy. Three floors of dust and chaos branched off the cobwebby staircase and even I could only improve them. Bicycles lay across the hall and landings and there was half a motor bike in the bathroom. One bedroom was full of easels and oil paints, another was full of horse brasses and saddles. There were fish tanks and hamster cages, mouse cages, fishing rods and outboard engines, guitars and trumpets and violins and a cardboard box full of incubating tortoise eggs in the airing cupboard. 'I don't know where to begin,' sighed the Water Bailiff's wife despairingly, as she led me through the muddle, closely followed by her three-year-old twins and a dog. I could see why she had found it difficult to get a serious cleaner to help her, but for me her house was wonderful, because for the first time in my life I could feel that my own home was quite orderly. 'Perhaps if you did a room at a time?' she suggested meekly. 'Whatever happens, you can't make things worse.' She gave me ten pounds to go up to the village and buy buckets and mops while she and the twins tore up old sheets for dusters. I decided to start at the top and work down.

I shifted bookcases, violin cases, mouse and hamster cages and an abstract sculpture made out of an old car engine on to the landing, rolled up my sleeves, filled my bucket with hot soapy water and began to scrub. I washed skirting boards and walls, scraped mould and unidentifiable scum off pipes, brushed hairy dust off ledges, hoovered into corners, emptied waste paper baskets full of rotting horror, shoved dirty washing into linen baskets and then put everything back. Tropical fish darted about, eyeing me with rage and trying to eat each other, the hamster snored and trembled in its nest of chewed tissue paper, the white mouse stared at me with its red eye. 'Look at that,' I said to it, 'that's me doing that. Me. I. Not some incompetent twit, only good for reading books and thinking thoughts and dreaming dreams. This is me, housecleaner and poacher.' The white mouse winked, the hamster woke up and trundled its wheel and the Water Bailiff's wife paid me ten pounds fifty.

I cleaned the house for three hours a morning two mornings a week and made the twenty-one pounds I earned last until Family Allowance day which carried us through to the weekends. Kate and Auntie invited me to go out poaching with them again, but I felt a certain moral perturbation about taking money from the Water Bailiff's wife at the same time as poaching her husband's river for the salmon. So I refused the invitation with regret and then began to worry in case Kate and Auntie thought I was a double agent. But Susie told me not to be so silly. Her own mother had, she told me, charred for the Water Bailiff's mother for years and the Water Bailiff's father had always gone poaching with Susie's father on his nights off. Susie added that she thought it was probably having a third class degree in Philosophy which had made me over-sensitive about ethics.

Chapter 26

'Tell us about yourself,' said the Income Support application form in a cosy voice. 'And about your partner. If you have one,' it added nastily. My mind shot back forty years to a Home Service programme called 'Music and Movement.' We used to glide and wave our arms about to it at primary school. 'Find a partner and move into a space,' the presenter used to say in a voice like the Queen's. Find a partner and move into a space. Easier said than done. No partner, no space, I thought and wrote 'N.A.' across the partner spaces.

I told the application form obediently about my name, age, address, title, marital status, National Insurance number (which I had, in a rare moment of efficiency, once written under my name in my address book), savings, nil, income, twenty-one pounds per week charring money (I didn't declare my earnings from poaching or Bingo), investments, nil. I signed a declaration that the information I had given was, to the best of my knowledge, true, and posted it. Three days later, it was posted back to me with a stiff note saying that I had neglected to send in any wages slips for the month. I sent it back explaining that you don't get wages slips for charring and so I hadn't got any.

Two days after that, a letter arrived telling me that the Government had worked out that as a lone parent (how dashing, as if I were galloping through life on a lean chestnut stallion) with one dependent child, I needed seventy-one pounds forty-three pence per week to live on. I was rather touched at the thought of the Government working this out for me, and I imagined it reading my application form in the House of Commons bar and deciding to give me seventy-one pounds forty-three pence per week.

The next day I got another letter. This one said that the Government had decided that as a lone parent with one dependent child, I needed thirty-five pounds seventeen pence per week to live on.

I rang the Income Support office to ask it what I had done in the last twenty-four hours to make the Government change its mind so dramatically about my needs. The Income Support girl laughed merrily. 'It's the computer,' she said.

I pointed out that the first letter, the seventy-one pounds forty-three pence one, was not written by computer but by human being.

That made the girl laugh even more. 'Ah,' she said, 'in that case, we won't have a record of it.'

'But you only sent it to me yesterday,' I protested.

'Yes, I know,' she said, 'but if it was handwritten, we won't have a copy of it. It has to be on the computer to be recorded.' She said that she would send me another application form to fill in.

'Tell us about yourself and your partner if you have one,' it said in its nasty, knowing, intimate way. It reminded me of soppy Gordon from 'Connect'. I told it about myself and posted it. Two days later, I got another letter. 'We regret to inform you,' it said, and the cosy tone had changed to one of cold bureaucratic triumph, 'that you are not eligible for Income Support.'

I rang up again and got a different girl. 'Why am I not eligible for Income Support?'

'I expect your savings are too high,' said the girl.

'I haven't got any savings,' I said.

'Oh,' said the girl, 'it must be your income then.'

'I earn twenty-one pounds per week,' I said.

'Tell you what,' said the girl, 'I'll send you another application form.'

I gave up. I could see why people turned to crime.

Chapter 27

Harriet failed her 'A' levels, said she'd never wanted to go
to university anyway and got a job making Cornish pasties
at Duncan's butcher's shop. I watched my friends' children
going away to take degrees in Psychology and Upholstery
and I wept for the mess I'd made of my family's lives.

Just before Christmas, one of Duncan's Improvers got flu
and there was panic in the sausage section. Harriet SOS'd
me. Did I want to earn a few casual quid quickly? It was not
my day for charring so I said yes I did, sent Sophie and her
packed lunch off to school and hurried round to Duncan's.

The sausage section was a cold room behind the shop
where pale intestines floated in small plastic buckets and a
huge mincer called the Butcher's Boy gobbled up slabs of
meat and regurgitated them into an enamel basin. I dressed
up in a white overall and a hat and watched Bill, the chief
sausage maker, mixing minced pork with pink rusk and
spice and loading it into the sausage machine. He drew a
sheep's intestine from its bucket and washed it carefully
under the tap. Then he fitted it tenderly over the nozzle of
the machine. About four yards of flimsy gut drooped from
the end of the nozzle. 'Just think,' said Bill, 'of the hundreds
of yards of that coiled up inside each and every one of us.' I
thought about it.

Bill talked me through. 'Press the throttle with your
thigh and squirt the sausage mix into the sheep's intestine.' I

pressed. The mixture exploded into the gut and blew it right off the nozzle and across the floor. 'Whoa . . . gently does it,' said Bill. 'Take it easy. It's all a question of pressure and timing. Watch.' He filled his intestine quickly and expertly and I watched, enthralled, as he pulled four yards of sausage off the nozzle, twisted and plaited it into six-inch chipolatas and hung the finished plait on to a hook.

Duncan came through from the shop and skidded on my exploded chipolata. 'Get a move on, you two, they're screaming for Cumberlands out there.'

Bill pulled a hog's intestine from its bucket and handed it to me. 'Bigger and stronger,' he explained, 'you'll probably get on better with this one.' I threaded the inside of the hog very carefully over the nozzle while Bill made up the Cumberland mix and loaded it into the sausage maker. With great caution, I pressed my right thigh gingerly against the throttle, made contact with the mince and watched with pride as my hog's intestine filled and bulged with Cumberland sausage. Four yards later I had run out of gut. Bill slipped the end off the nozzle and began to knit and twist the four-yard sausage into sections. I watched carefully. 'Pinch it, squeeze it, pull it up and under, twist it, thread it through and loop it up in threes,' he chanted, fitting the actions to the words. Pinch it, squeeze it, pull it up and under, twist it, thread it through and loop it up in threes. It was like a country dance or a magic spell. We stood in front of the Butcher's Boy, reciting our in-cantation, pinching and squeezing, twisting and threading and looping until I got it right at last and my own unaided plait of sausages swung from the hook above the sink.

We made eighty pounds of sausages in the first hour. No sooner had we slung them over the hooks than Duncan rushed in and disappeared into the shop with them. I thought of the households who would be dining on my handiwork that night. Five hours later I walked out through the shop and turned to look back at the window. There they were, hanging in proud lines, my sausages. I stood on the pavement and watched as Duncan reached up and cut off half a dozen and weighed them up for Lady Hennessey, who had no idea at all that I had worked backstage again to make her supper. Supplier of salmon and sausages to the aristocracy of Honeyford. It was a start.

Chapter 28

The heart and stomach of the old Andante blazed on through all the crises and vicissitudes of my life, but eventually the strain began to tell, and though her engine was as brave as ever, her body started to rust and shake and fall apart. Not like me, I thought. With me, it's the engine that goes before the body. The day came when the garage man who MOT'd her told me gently that it was going to cost four times as much as she was worth to get her through the test, and though I would have paid it if I'd got it, I hadn't, and I had to let her go. I patted her on the bonnet and caught a bus home.

There was a poster stuck on to the glass partition behind the driver's head. 'Why not be a minibus driver?' it asked. Why not indeed? I thought it would be better paid than charring and memorised the number to ring for further information.

Three weeks later, I went to the bus station to find out whether or not I had it in me to become a minibus driver. In the Chief Instructor's office, I had to fill in a form about my age, qualifications, hobbies, health and criminal record. 'Why hobbies?' I asked.

'Plenty of interests shows you are a well-rounded person who can cope with strain,' explained the Chief Instructor.

I decided not to mention that I had gone mad when my marriage broke up. But at the end of the form was a note which said that the deliberate withholding of any relevant information was a criminal offence and punishable by law. I began to sweat with guilt and was just about to say I'd changed my mind and wanted to go home when the door opened and the Chief Instructor introduced me to my Personal Instructor.

'This is Mr Eeles,' he said. Mr Eeles gazed at me through slitty and unfriendly eyes and I recognised him as Conger Eeles, the boy who'd telephoned the school to say that he had planted a bomb and had caused me to risk my life to save Wayne Foggin and Glenda Dawson's duck. I looked into his nasty face and remembered that he had been excluded for bullying and extortion and that he'd made my life a misery when he was in the second form. He was the one who sneered, who spat, who chewed, who answered back and swore and put his feet up on the library tables and wrote obscenities upon the lavatory walls. And as I remembered all those things, I knew that Conger Eeles was remembering them too. For five years he had tortured younger boys and novice teachers, and now here he was, a driving instructor, about to teach me how to drive a bus. My guilt about withholding information evaporated. If Conger Eeles could pass his driving test, so could I.

He narrowed his slitty eyes still more and bared his teeth in a nasty smile. 'Pleased to meet you,' he said, and there was an unspoken agreement that we would both pretend that we had never met before.

But years of mutual dislike simmered and swelled until they cracked the surface as we sat side by side in the cabin of that minibus, and the air around us was electric with tense loathing.

'All right,' said Conger Eeles, and I could hear the oily malice in his voice, 'you can set your vehicle into motion.'

'Does that mean I can start her up?' I asked childishly. Conger Eeles merely nodded his flat head. I turned the ignition key and felt seventeen-and-a-half feet of minibus jerk into gear beneath me.

'Dear me,' smirked Conger Eeles, 'we'll have to do better than that, won't we? If my granny had been standing up at the back with all her shopping bags, she'd have been thrown off her feet, wouldn't she, with a start like that?'

'I would hope,' I replied, in a schoolmarmy voice, 'that someone would have had the decency to offer her a seat.' That shut him up for a minute.

'Take the first left off the next roundabout.' I did as I was told and bumbled into a 'Buses only' section of the town, jerking along towards a stop. 'Right,' whispered Conger, and I signalled right. 'No,' he sneered, delighted to have fooled me, 'I didn't mean right turn right, I mean right, now I want you to pull into that bus stop.' I signalled left and got blasted by a real bus driver who was following us with his radiator practically up my exhaust pipe. I pulled in at the stop and Conger Eeles stretched his mouth into a mocking leer and pointed out that the two-foot gap between my bus and the curb would be beyond his granny. 'You should always halt your vehicle in a straight line no more than six inches from and parallel with the curb,' he sighed. In a fit of pique I pressed a red button and the door of the bus concertinaed back and a very agile old lady leapt aboard.

'Sorry Madam, I'm not in service,' said Conger Eeles with smarmy charm.

The old lady was deaf. 'Senior Citizen's return to the Piper's Pudding,' she shouted.

'I said "We're not in service",' repeated Conger.

'How much?' asked the old lady, smiling perkily at me.

'I'm a learner driver,' I shouted, 'I'm not safe.'

'Too bloody right,' hissed Conger, smiling through his teeth at my would-be passenger. He took her by the elbow and steered her off the bus, shut the door and directed me out to an industrial estate on the edge of town.

'Stop the bus here and we'll do some fare-taking exercises.' There was power in his voice and I knew that he was loving this. He nipped round to the top step of the bus, put on a squeaky voice and asked if he could have an adult return to the Piper's Pudding.

Of course he could, I replied, and waited to be told what to do.

'Press AR for Adult Return, press eighty-eight for Piper's Pudding, press Issue for issue and the fare'll come up on the screen and the ticket'll come out of the slot,' said Conger very quickly.

I pressed everything in sight and jammed the machine. 'What the hell is the Piper's Pudding anyway?'

'It's a fare stage,' he said pityingly as he unjammed the machine. I realised that he was getting his own back for years of humiliation at being labelled a Slow Learner, but that didn't alter the fact that he was, and always had been, loathsome. He turned himself into two Senior Citizens on Explorer Tickets, three children and a dog, one student return and somebody who had got on between stops. I couldn't do any of them, and I knew what it felt like to be a slow learner.

Conger Eeles had not finished with me yet. 'You have to do a braking exercise,' he said, curving his long neck and writhing with snaky glee. 'It's a kind of emergency stop but not so violent if you get my meaning. That's because my granny is still stood up at the back of the bus and we don't want to catapult her through the windscreen, do we?' We probably did, but we kept our mouth shut. 'What I want you to do,' said Conger, 'is to drive the vehicle along the highway at a steady forty miles per hour, then, when I tell you to, and only when I tell you to, I want you to apply the brakes firmly and bring the vehicle to a halt within twenty-seven feet.' His slitty eyes glittered and his sharp teeth flashed and I hated him. 'Now,' hissed Conger Eeles.

I slammed on the brakes as violently as I possibly could and he fell over. A red light shone in his evil eye as he got up, and his voice was menacing.

'You always were a stupid cow,' he spat.

'You always were a vile bully,' I replied. I was cold and calm as I shoved the bus into gear and roared away.

'Where are you going?' hissed Conger, and this time I heard fear. I said nothing, but drove the bus faster and faster, swerving round bends on the industrial estate until I found what I was looking for.

'Private Property. This land is patrolled by Pike and Stapler Ltd. Wheelclamps in operation.' said the notice. I parked my bus six inches away from the curb, right underneath and perfectly parallel to the notice, took the key out of the ignition and jumped down from the driving seat.

'Lovely to meet you again, Darren,' I said, waving the keys merrily at him, and I left him, open-mouthed and finally defeated, to explain to Pike and Stapler why he had parked his bus beneath their notice.

It was a two-mile walk back to the bus station. I marched into the Chief Instructor's office and handed him my keys. 'Mr Eeles got a bit held up,' I said. 'I expect you'll be hearing from him soon.' I turned to leave and the door swung open.

A tiny, very tough and very angry old lady flew in, quivering on high heels and swinging her handbag with rage. 'I'm Mr Eeles's granny,' she squawked at the Chief Instructor, who had taken cover behind the desk. 'My Darren telephoned me half an hour ago from a telephone box on the Lower Marsh Estate. Some madwoman has run off with the keys to his bus and he's been wheelclamped and I've come to sort you lot out.' She took a swipe at him with her handbag. We were fighters, Conger Eeles's granny and I.

Chapter 29

It must have been the following Sunday, after church, when Sophie and I walked up to Jenkins' farm to buy some free-range eggs from Susie. There was no one in the kitchen, so we wandered round into the yard to look for her. The chickens fussed at our feet and the dogs scratched lazily in the sun, but there was still no sign of Susie. 'She's probably learning new chords in the caravan,' said Sophie pityingly. A sad noise floated out of a barn. 'Sounds like a cow in labour,' Sophie said. It was.

Harold Jenkins, Susie's father-in-law, stood beside the cow who was standing unhappily at the far end of the barn. He took off his cap and wiped his sweating forehead with the back of his hand. 'She's got problems,' he said. 'I'll have to go in and help her if she don't get going soon.' When she heard Harold's voice, the cow turned her head to look at him pleadingly and called to him in a long, drawn-out moan.

'Where are Mike and Susie?' I asked.

'Mike's seeing to a fence on the far side of the valley and Susie's vanished,' said Harold crossly. The cow stretched out her neck and strained, opening her mouth and tensing her face until her tongue stuck out.

'Her eyes are popping,' said Sophie in a horrified whisper.

'I'll go and get a bucket of water,' said Harold. Sophie

and I waited helplessly, feeling useless and not knowing what to do. We had only come to buy a dozen eggs.

Harold came back with a bucket of water, took off his cap and rolled up his sleeves. 'Pass me that soap off the ledge,' he ordered. He soaped his arm until it was white and slippery from the finger tips up to the elbow and then he slid it gently into the cow. 'You mustn't go in too early,' he said quietly. 'Makes 'em lazy and then they give up. Come on, my darling,' he murmured to the cow. 'All right my lovely, you'll be all right, my girl.'

Sophie and I stood mesmerised, watching his arm as it turned and felt and soothed inside the cow. 'He's stuck, my beauty, isn't he? Hold on old lady, while I turn his head for you.' He slid his arm out of the cow and walked to the other end of the barn. He cut two lengths of binder twine and picked up a slim iron rod.

Sophie gulped. 'Is he going to stick that in her?' she whispered.

The same thought had occurred to me. 'Don't be daft,' I whispered back.

The arm was back inside the cow and Harold was working carefully and silently. Sophie and I didn't dare to move or speak. And then I saw the first hoof, cream-coloured and soft, sticking out. The animal groaned and arched her head back; her eyes were wide and bursting with pain. I thought, 'Oh God, I hope she doesn't die, not with Sophie watching. Not with me watching.'

Then I forgot about Sophie and everything else when Harold said, 'Come here'. He had slipped a double length of binder twine around the little hoof and now he was holding out the taut ends to me. 'Don't pull,' he said, 'just hold it steady so the hoof can't slip back. She's too tired to help much now.' He drew out the other hoof, slipped a second noose of binder twine around it and passed the taut ends to me. 'Hang on tight,' he ordered, 'but you mustn't pull. I'm going to get some grease.' For a long minute Sophie and I were left alone with the life-and-death responsibility, but then he was back with a great white wodge of grease in his hand. 'I always grease the head,' he said. 'Some fools try to pull 'em out dry, but that's terrible for the cow. Bruises and breaks her up inside.' He reached in past the hoofs and we watched the movements of his arm and wrist as his hand curved and soothed and smoothed the grease around the unseen head.

Then it was time for the iron bar. He took the four taut lengths of binder twine from me and tied them quickly and deftly round the centre of the bar. 'You take the left side, I'll go on the right.' We knelt side by side in the wet straw. 'Now take it easy,' Harold said. 'This is where people go wrong. They go mad and pull too fast and hurt the cow. Wait till I tell you, then pull till I say to stop. Now.' I pulled on my end of the bar. It took all my strength. 'Now stop,' said Harold. I remembered the midwife when Sophie was being born. 'Push . . . now relax . . . push again . . .' and I tuned into the rhythm of the animal's labour. 'Pull,' said Harold, 'and stop . . . pull again . . .' and again we hauled together on the slim iron bar. Two front legs slid out. 'That's beautiful,' said Harold, 'hold her there a minute . . . now . . . again.' A nose appeared, slippery with mucus. Two more pulls and the head was out, covered by a mask of mucus, apparently not breathing. An eyelid fluttered. 'Harder,' ordered Harold. I leaned back as far as I could go, gritting my teeth, unaware of everything except the need to pull.

Shoulders and body shot out in a rush and a big brown calf skidded across the floor and I fell over backwards. I scrambled up and cleared the mucus from her nose and mouth and then she was gurgling and breathing. Harold slipped the binder twine from one of the wet front legs and pumped hard to get the calf's circulation going. 'You take the other leg and do the same,' he said. 'We've got to get her heart working properly.'

The cow staggered to her feet and watched us working on her baby. When we had finished, she took over and began the long, slow patient task of licking the calf clean and dry and warm. I stood there for a long time holding Sophie's hand, dazed with the pride of what I had helped to do.

'Lucky you was here,' said Harold, washing his hands and putting on his cap. 'They would 'a died without you.'

Chapter 30

Sausage maker, salmon poacher, gambler, char, midwife to the bovine and bus driver; I had learned at last that the meaning and purpose of life is survival; but it was not enough. 'There's something missing,' I said to Jean and Susie, 'but I can't think what it is.'

The old woman from the café waddled into my mind. It had been a long time since I had thought about her. 'You do just what you want to do,' she said. 'But I don't know what that is,' I replied and opened the evening paper to look through the 'Situations Vacant' column. 'Artists and Writers wanted for Greetings Cards. Send stamped addressed envelope for samples and information.' 'There you are,' said the old Baglady.

I sent off a stamped and addressed envelope for samples and information and waited excitedly for it to come back. When it did, the sample cards turned out to be very rude, and Jean and Susie and I were rather shocked by them. Still, as Jean said, everyone has to begin somewhere, and as Susie added, it's all right to prostitute your art to pay the bills. There would be time for Art and Integrity after the Poll Tax.

I shut myself up in Shangri-la for the morning and designed a brilliant and witty Get Well Soon card. It showed a district nurse arriving at a house clutching a lot of rubber tubing and a kettle of hot water. The caption underneath said: 'The Enema at the Gate. Get Well Soon.' We laughed for days and waited for a cheque and eager orders to fall through the letter box.

But the card company sent my idea back, saying that it wasn't quite what they had had in mind. 'Too sophisticated,' said Jean consolingly.

I walked to the Water Bailiff's house feeling dejected. Was this how it was going to be from now on? Was I always going to be scratching a living without much point to it, earning just enough to survive, living without dreams?

Nola Gleeson swayed down the street towards me. 'All right, my duck? You look a bit fed up.'

'I'm all right Nola, thanks. It's just that sometimes you wonder where it's all going to end.'

Nola put her arms round me. I could smell the alcohol. 'Trust to the Lord,' she said and hiccupped. 'He moves in a Mysterious Way.' She moved off in an equally mysterious way and I went to do my charring.

That evening, there was a knock on the door and Nola stood in the porch, clutching a brown paper bag. The smell of alcohol surrounded her like a halo. 'I've brought you my Bible to read,' she wheezed. 'Thought it might cheer you up.' She refused my offer of a cup of tea and disappeared into the night.

There they were, all those heroes and villains from childhood, God and Satan, Adam and Eve, Noah, David and Goliath. I flicked through Nola's Bible, smiling at the garish pictures, remembering Sunday School and Sodom and Gomorrah and the earnest spinsters with plaits around their heads who had told us the stories with such burning conviction.

In the middle of the night, I woke up with a rhyme thundering through my head.

Sodom and Gomorrah (it pounded)
You're fillin' me with horrah,
Sodom and Gomorrah
I'll burn you up tomorrah
You'll be shriekin' with sorrah
In Sodom and Gomorrah.

I got up and went downstairs to find a pen and paper, jotted down the words and went back to bed. In the morning I looked at them and they made me laugh, so I bought a cheap exercise book on the way to do battle with the Water Bailiff's house.

All through that morning words and rhymes and rhythms kept jumping and wriggling into my head. I was swabbing the bathroom floor, trying to remember what was in the fridge at home, when God suddenly yelled,

I'm gonna blot out man from the face of the
earth,
I'm gonna drown 'em all, 'cos they just ain't
worth
The trouble I took, it was all in vain,
So heavens! Am I gonna make it rain.

I shooed a spider out of the bath and blew it through the window.

But just before He made it pour,
God looked down, then He looked once more,
Saw one righteous man sitting in his garden,
And God yelled 'Noah!'
And Noah said 'Pardon?'

I dropped the bath cleaner and ran for my exercise book. A

slow worm slithered across the floor towards me.

> Along came a serpent,
> (A very civil serpent)
> Whispered to Eve,
> 'Would you believe
> I've got a trick or two up my sleeve?'

I caught the slow worm and delivered it out into the garden. It looked at me gratefully and disappeared into a hedge.

That afternoon I sat in Shangri-la with Nola Gleeson's Bible and my exercise book and pencil and began to re-write the Old Testament.

For days and days, whenever I wasn't charring or shopping or hoovering or child-collecting, I sat in Shangri-la and wrote the Bible.

Then one morning the door opened and Susie's head poked through. 'Oh sorry,' she said, 'I didn't realise you were here. What are you doing?'

I sat back and looked at what I was doing. I was sitting in an old blue caravan in the middle of a field writing Bible stories in jingly verse.

'What are you up to?' asked Susie again.

'Just writing a few letters,' I lied. Even my best friends could not be told about the Bible. I scooped it up into a plastic bag and got up. 'Your turn,' I said to Susie. 'What are you up to?'

She blushed and tried unsuccessfully to hide a guitar behind her back. 'Nothing much,' she said.

I tried to stop writing the Bible, but it kept on coming at me. What was I going to do about it? Was it a mild talent or a mild curse or just a lot of mediocre nonsense? In the end I went to see the Vicar.

Chapter 31

Our Vicar is wild and handsome and he once turned down a
scholarship to RADA and went to Theological College
instead. I knocked on the Vicarage door and left my Bible
with his wife who promised to give it to him as soon as he
got home from cheering up the latest divorcee.

The next morning he phoned me. 'I like it. I like it
enormously. The question is, what are we going to do about
it?' I told him I'd hoped he would be able to tell me that.
'Leave it with me for a day or two. I'll contact you when I
get a vision.'

Three days later he had a vision and he beamed it to me
excitedly down the telephone. 'I'll do it as a serial instead of
preaching a sermon at matins.' He was really alight.

'Like the Archers?'

'Can you do some more?' the Vicar went on. 'Cain and
Abel and the Tower of Babel and Moses and Jacob and
Esau?'

As soon as he'd rung off, I rushed round to Shangri-la. It
felt like going out to work, going out to do a real job, but a
million times better than any other job I'd ever had. I
settled down with Nola's Bible and thought about the
beginning of things.

> In the Beginning was the Word
> 'Oy,' said the word, but nobody heard.

'Hello,' said Susie, 'you've beaten me to it again.'

Because the jingles had been approved by the Vicar, I felt safe to show them to Susie. It was difficult for her at first because her family has been fearfully religious in a devoutly superstitious, non-churchgoing way for generations, and I could tell that she was shocked. Then she began to giggle. 'Well,' she said in the end, 'if the Vicar says it's all right, I suppose it must be. I just hope you don't get clouted by a thunderbolt. When's he going to do it?'

He did the first episode two Sundays later in a high wind. Susie and Jean met me at the end of the street and we walked up to the church together. I appreciated their support because I knew that they only ever went to church for weddings and christenings and funerals.

'I do think you're brave,' muttered Susie as we got inside the porch.

'The Vicar's a brilliant performer,' I muttered back, 'I know he'll make it sound good.'

'I didn't mean that,' said Susie. 'I meant God. What if He thinks it's blasphemous? There's a hell of a gale blowing up the river.' A great sock of wind bashed itself against the church tower. 'Oh God,' said Susie.

The organist struck up the opening hymn, which was, of course, 'God Moves in a Mysterious Way,' and the choir processed down the nave. I looked at the backs of the necks of the congregation: the upright Brigadier and the squat Squadron Leader and their tall and poised and well-groomed wives; three earnest spinsters, wise and woolly virgins who did good works throughout the parish on their bicycles; the village whore who did her own good works in her own way on her own bicycle; a small-time Mr Big who bought and sold houses to make huge profits between Monday and Saturday and who cleaned his soul and his car on Sundays; a peppering of widows and a clutch of duffle-coated mothers with trendy toddlers.

We sang and confessed our ways through the service until the Vicar climbed the steps of the pulpit for the sermon. 'In the name of the Father,' he called, and the wind hurled itself at the tower, 'and of the Son,' and the rain beat against the stained-glass angels, 'and of the Holy Ghost,' and the church lights dipped and dimmed.

'In the Beginning was the Word,' announced the Vicar; the church lights flickered, grew steady and shone on.

> 'Oy,' said the Word, but nobody heard.
> 'Humph,' said the Word, and tried again,
> But the echo only sighed 'Amen.'
> The Word said,
> 'I'm fed
> Up with no one to talk to,'
> The Word said,
> 'I'm fed
> Up with nowhere to walk to.'

The congregation sat very still and amazed. Even the trendy toddlers stopped playing with their construction kits of the Parables and tapped their mini Doc Martens against the pews.

The Brigadier's back grew more and more upright and his lady looked disdainful. The village bicyclists winked at each other and grinned and the Mr Big shuffled his backside and cleared his throat.

The Vicar's voice rang out.

'Eve, Eve, that was a big mistake.
You'll get more than just a tummy ache.'

'In the name of the Father and of the Son and of the Holy Ghost, Amen,' he added as he left the pulpit and turned upstage for the Creed.

Chapter 32

The village buzzed with the story.

The widows and the wise and woolly virgins loved it and rode their bicycles to the Vicarage to congratulate the Vicar. The whore, the Mr Big, the Brigadier and the Squadron Leader were shocked and angry and called meetings at each other's houses to decide what should be done. In the end, the Squadron Leader and the whore drafted a stiff note of disapproval to the Bishop and sent a copy of it to the Parish Magazine, which is edited by the Chief Virgin, and so another meeting was called in her house to draft a letter of approval to the Bishop and the Parish Magazine.

The following Sunday, for the first time in years, the church was packed to its back pews. People who had never entered it since their own christenings and who had never planned to do so again until their funerals had heard the tale of how the Vicar was reading blasphemous verse from the pulpit, and now they were queueing at the doors before opening time.

This time he gave them Noah:

> They came to rest on Mount Ararat,
> Just fancy that, Mount Ararat.
> Noah climbed out and he took off his hat

And he said,
'Well Lord, that appears to be that.'

and a bit of Moses:

> The Pharoah of Egypt was anti the Jews;
> He called all his soldiers about him.
> He said, 'Listen everyone, here is the news,
> I'm the Pharoah and I can do just what I choose,
> And I've had quite enough of these howling
>   Hebrews,
> So my view is, we're better without 'em.'

The congregation burst into spontaneous applause, but the Brigadier, the Squadron Leader, the whore and the Mr Big stalked angrily and ostentatiously out of the church.

On the following Sunday, the pews were packed again. The Vicar climbed the steps of the pulpit and began with his usual flair.

'Sodom and Gomorrah,'

he roared in the voice of the Lord,

> 'I'm gonna have to write the Torah.
> Sodom and Gomorrah
> You're fillin' me with horrah.
> Sodom and Gomorrah
> I'll burn you up tomorrah.
> You'll be shriekin' with sorrah
> In Sodom and Gomorrah.'

'An Angel said to Lot, . . .'

Everybody leaned forward, agog to hear what the angel had to say, but suddenly the Vicar's voice faltered and faded, and he seemed to lose his way in the script. His eyes were fixed in shock on the pew where an elderly man with white hair was sitting in a long black overcoat. 'An angel said to L . . . L . . .' stammered the Vicar, but the words refused to come. The man in the long black coat got up and walked down the nave towards the pulpit. 'Oh my God, it's God,' whispered Susie.

But it wasn't God, it was the Bishop, who, having been bombarded with contradictory letters from Brigadiers, virgins and whores, had disguised himself as a member of the congregation of St Eustace's and had come to see for himself. He smiled at the Vicar. 'May I?' he asked. The Vicar almost curtsied as he handed my manuscript to his boss.

The Bishop took a deep breath.

> An angel said to Lot,
> 'You'd better get out,
> Take your wife and your daughters and flee.
> Don't look back, for without any doubt,
> Fire and brimstone are going to spout
> Over Sodom. You can take it from me.'
> Alas and alack
> Lot's wife turned back.
> Lot's wife turned into a pillar of salt.
> But God said,
> 'Well, it was her own silly fault.'

The Bishop bowed to the applause, produced his mitre from underneath his coat, plonked it on his head and did a little tap dance. 'In the name of the Father . . .' he began, before he led the way into the Creed.

Chapter 33

What do you do after you've written the Bible? Where is there to go after that? The question made me restless and I put the choke-chain on Mistake and walked crossly to the Co-op. As I hitched the end of her lead over the Post Office railings, I glanced at the advertisement window.

'American Families seek Typical English Homes to rent through July/August.' There was an agency name and telephone number and I copied them down and took them home.

'It's a very good idea,' said Sophie. 'Americans pay loads of money to stay in quaint old English houses in quaint old English villages like this.'

I looked doubtfully at the house. 'Would you call this quaint?'

'No,' said Sophie, 'I'd call it shabby. But the Americans'll call it charming and atmospheric and they'll pay us enough money to paint it up afterwards so it won't be shabby any more.' It seemed very logical.

'But where would the rest of us go for the summer?'

'Shangri-la, of course,' said Sophie.

Harriet and Jane said thank you very much but they would prefer to rent a room in Tarminster.

I walked across the fields to look at Shangri-la. There she squatted, old and blue, with her tall chimney and her woodburning stove, as unsuitable as ever for towing. She would do for Sophie and Mistake and me for July and August. I went home, dialled the agency number and fixed a date for the agent to come and inspect us.

All that charring at the Water Bailiff's house had not been wasted. I could clean a house as well as the next man now. I scrubbed floors and skirting boards and basins and threw out twenty years' worth of broken toys, unwearable clothes and unplayable games. Sophie found the old puppets in a sack at the back of a cupboard and I put them in the dustbin. 'Don't throw those away,' she said, rescuing them, 'you made those.' But the pram went into a skip in another street at dead of night when nobody was looking.

The agent was predictably enchanted by our quaint and atmospheric home, untrammelled as it was by the vices of modern life. Vices like dishwashers and tumble dryers and microwave ovens. It was exactly what his clients wanted, he cried, looking at me as if I were the last remnant of a dying civilization.

And then, ten days later, a cheque for an absurdly huge amount of money fell through the letterbox. For the first time in years, I had some real money. I went to look at Shangri-la again. It was a terrible day: rain poured relentlessly on to and into her; damp patches formed in her ceiling, drips wriggled down her walls and windows, the wind whistled through her door frame. I shivered and wondered what I'd done.

But the cheque was in the bank and a chunk of real money does wonders for the imagination and the courage.

The first lot of Americans arrived and settled into our quaint and atmospheric home with cries of joy. Sophie and Mistake and I moved into Shangri-la and waited for the school term to end. Then Charley's mother rang to say they'd booked a cottage in Cornwall for three weeks from the beginning of the summer holidays and could Sophie and Mistake go with them. 'Please, Mum,' begged Sophie.

So suddenly there would be nobody at all with me in Shangri-la. Suddenly it would be me. On my own.

'You don't mind, do you, Mum?'

'Of course I don't,' I lied.

All those partings at the school gates had been leading up to this. I was alone and free. Quite, quite free.

I lay on my back on Shangri-la's end bunk and gazed out of the window across the open fields to the hills and the sky. I remembered a landscape I had travelled twenty-three years earlier, where open countryside and hopping hills and a high white road had stretched to the skyline and the sea. I lay on my back in Shangri-la dreaming of the hills and the high white road.

It sparkled in the sunshine, running and swooping on and on into the sky. Twenty-three years ago I had been freewheeling carelessly along it towards something that had somehow become a marriage.

The road climbed on and up and over another hill. There was no need now to decide where I was going, where it was leading, where it would end; no need to fit things in, no one to fit things in for. No reason to do anything at all except dream on and on along this high, white road.

Chapter 34

I woke up with a jerk and a stiff neck. What on earth was I doing? Where was I? What time was it? Where had everybody gone? The sun was setting behind the hills, I had no food for supper, I had missed the shops. What a fool I was. Only I could be this impractical, this irresponsible. And then I realised with glee that it didn't matter. Nobody would suffer for it. Nobody would even know. Jane and Harriet were doubtless cooking brown rice and bean-sprouts in their room in Tarminster and Sophie was probably dining out in some chic fish restaurant in Cornwall. Charley's mother was better than I was at being divorced. She somehow managed to be rich, to go on holidays, to eat out in restaurants. 'But anybody can be rich,' I said angrily to Shangri-la, 'it's not some sodding God-given talent, some Divine Right. Even I could be rich if I had the money.'

And then I remembered that I had.

I *had* got money.

This was me.

I was rich.

At least for a week or two. Money meant that I could buy clothes and microwaves and videos and shoes and hairdos and things and things and things and meals out. Was that what it was all about, then? Was that where the white road led? To things and shoes and meals out?

But it also meant that I could just *be*. Oh, that was it. Just be. At last I could step aside, draw a breath, look at the view, have time to stand and stare. I was on holiday. Holiday. Holy Day.

I let my mind unwind and stretch and wander. I looked back down the long years of washing and shopping and gambling and puppeteering to the thrill of the day when Teapot had won his race, to the battles with the kitchen floor, to the day when I bought Shangri-la, the day I realised that Roger didn't want me, the day my tooth broke off and the flight into the hospital. I thought about Nola Gleeson and the night I'd won three times at Bingo when God had moved in a mysterious way. I remembered the poaching, the charring, the bus driving, the Bishop and the Bible. I thought about the wonderful moment when I had helped Harold Jenkins to deliver the calf. And now here I was, in my caravan, on my high white road, going . . . going . . .?

The words came flying and skidding into my mind. I grabbed my bag and found an old shopping list and a biro and I caught the words and wrote them down before they could escape.

> You won't get the OBE
> For being you and me,
> For being ordinary and making beds.
> And there's no award from Booker
> When you've cleaned the bloody cooker
> And you've poured that green shampoo on nitty
>   heads.
>
> That's why some of us go crazy and others take
>   to drink,
> And some of us screw

The man from the Pru,
Or take up pen and ink.

We want to be exciting and inviting, fly-
    by-nighting,
We want to be exotic and erotic, Pavarottic;
We need a bit of glamour, bit of sparkle, bit of
    glitter,
Bit of something-round-the-corner when we're
    sitting in the litter.

Loud applause and celebrations,
Fun and scandalous sensations,
Telegrams, congratulations,
Recognition from the nations.

So we grind our teeth and mutter as we cut the
    bread and butter
And we wait for life to yawn and stretch and
    give his wings a flutter.

I sat back. 'The Song of the Sink' I wrote across the top of
it. And that was that.

From then on, wherever I was, walking by the river,
bicycling along the lanes, swimming in the sea, bussing into
Tarminster, the words kept coming at me and I began to
carry a small notebook and a biro everywhere I went. The
words swung and giggled into my mind: odes for wild
spinsters, laments for abandoned wives, a catchy little
number called, 'I'm in Love with the Undertaker but I
think he only Wants me for my Body,' and something
called 'Young Mother Blues' which I dedicated with love
to all those who recognised the symptoms:

I want to be snug,
I want to be smug,
I want to be hugged-up, fugged-up
Snug-as-a-bug-in-a-rug.

I want to be kind.
I want to be good,
I want to be happy changing nappies,
Cooking food.

I want to be calm.
I want to be sweet.
I want to be patient, cosy,
Nice and clean and neat.

But
I'm

Big and bad and cross and wild,
I scream and shake my awful child.
I shoot the china off the shelf.
(One day I nearly shot myself.)
I long to go and get blind drunk
And have an orgy with a monk.
I dream I've bombed the Toddler Club
And danced a striptease down the pub.

But

I want to be snug,
I want to be smug,
I want to be hugged-up-fugged-up
Snug-as-a-bug-in-a-rug.

But the best one of all burst out of the air one day in the middle of one of Tarminster's shopping precincts, which looked like every other shopping precinct in every other town with its mediocre supermarket, its pessimistic charity shop, its garish video shop, its awe-inspiring sex-shop and its Pay and Display car park. 'This is not what life ought to be about,' I said to a Traffic Warden who was sticking a Fixed Penalty notice on to a beige Mini which had been parked for too long outside the charity shop.

'I quite agree with you,' said the Traffic Warden.

A Good Woman ran out of the charity shop where she had been working, saw the Fixed Penalty notice on her car, swore and burst into tears. 'Bloody hell,' she said, 'what is the use of trying to be upright and kind and doing Good shagging Works when all you get in return is a Fixed Penalty notice?'

'I quite agree with you,' said the Traffic Warden again and she stared wildly about her, ripped the notice off the Good Woman's car and threw it into the gutter. 'I hate this job,' she said.

The Good Woman blew her nose.

'What would you have liked to have been if you could have been anything you wanted?' she asked.

'I wanted to be Miss England,' the Traffic Warden confessed. 'I was Miss Tarminster once. In 1965. I wanted to go on.' She blushed. I looked at her in her hat and her brogues and her jacket and skirt and tried to imagine her slinking across the stage of Tarminster Town Hall, wearing a swimsuit and high heels and telling the judges that her ambition was to travel and then to be a missionary.

The Good Woman cheered up. 'I always wanted to be a tart,' she confided, 'a real one in underwear and suspenders under a red light in a window in Amsterdam. But I never had the nerve, so I married the Methodist Minister and became a Good Woman instead.'

'Oh well,' said the Traffic Warden, 'I'd better get on, I suppose.' She plodded off down the street.

The Good Woman watched her go and then she climbed into her Mini and roared off at great speed the wrong way round the one-way system.

I sat down on a wooden seat beside an apologetic fountain and I thought of all the women that I knew, the good ones, the bad ones, the brave ones and the timid ones, and I wrote this song for all of us. I called it 'The Song of the Good Woman'.

I'm going to be a beauty queen,
I'm going to be a star;
I'm going to burst upon the scene
In my brand-new fork-lift bra.

I'm going to shave my hairy shins
I'm going to flash my thighs;
I'm going to shed my double chins,
And sparkle up my eyes.

I'm going to chuck the Brownie Pack,
I'm stuffing CAB,
I'm giving all Good Works the sack
To concentrate on me.

So don't tell me your troubles.
Don't load me with your trust.
I'm only froth and bubbles,
I'm just here for the lust.

So look out, World, I'm coming.
Hey look out, World, it's me.
I'll set your pulses drumming,
And I'm only forty-three.

Which wasn't strictly true, but it rhymed.

As soon as I saw it written down, I knew that this was it. This was what I could do. This was real. At last I knew what I was: I was a pop songwriter.

Chapter 35

The Radio Two disc jockey on the little transistor in Shangri-la was playing Golden Oldies from the Fifties. Jim Dale, Tommy Steele and Adam Faith asked me what did I want if I didn't want money, told me that the party was over and then said that they'd never felt more like singing the blues.

I jived genteelly with Shangri-la's broom until Elvis begged me not to step on his blue suede shoes. In an instant I was back at the High School. It was Wet Break in 4A and Judith Littlewick, Susie, Jean and I were dancing frantically to Elvis, singing and rocking and rolling on and off the teacher's table while the others perched on the radiators and the desks, hand-jiving and clapping and harmonising. We had been the sparklers of 4A, the four of us; we were the stars, the baddies who sang and danced and made the others laugh, who did Latin and RI and Rock 'n' Roll for 'O' level. We should have been singers and dancers and strippers, but you don't get put on the High School Honours Board for that.

I hugged the broom and howled along with Elvis. I howled for us and for all those like us, for all the traffic wardens who should have been beauty queens, for all the worthy women who should have been tarts, for all those with third class degrees who had locked up their wildness and played for safety.

Elvis stopped and so did I. I switched off the little transistor and thought in the silence. It might be too late for the Traffic Warden and the Good Woman, but it was not too late for me. It was never too late to be a pop songwriter.

I jumped out of Shangri-la and went in search of Susie. She was finishing the milking, so I helped her to wallop the last cow back into the field and sluice down the milking parlour and then I called a meeting. We rang Jean who said she would meet us in Shangri-la in half an hour as soon as she'd finished making canapés for a wedding and put them into the freezer. She said she'd bring a bottle of wine.

'I want to read you something,' I said when we were all together and drinking the wine in Shangri-la. And then I gave them 'Young Mother Blues', 'The Song of the Sink', and 'The Song of the Good Woman'.

There was a long, stunned silence.

At last Jean said, 'Do you remember us at school?'

'Go on,' I said.

'You two and Judith Littlewick and me,' said Jean.

'Rocking and rolling on the teacher's table,' said Susie.

'Go on,' I said.

'It was wonderful, wasn't it?' said Susie dreamily. 'We were very good at it, you know.'

There was another long, thoughtful pause.

And then, 'That was always, deep down, what I really wanted to be,' said Jean.

'Go on,' I said.

'Ever since those 4A Wet Breaks. More than anything else in the world, I wanted to be a pop star. That was what I could never admit to Kevin when he gave up being a Rising Executive and turned into a woodcarver. How could I tell him then, just when he needed me to be sensible? But that was what I always wanted.'

'Me too,' said Susie and she twanged on her guitar.

We sat and stared at one another.

'It seems to me,' said Jean at last, 'that it's now or never. We didn't have the nerve to try it in the first half of our lives, so we'd better have the nerve to try it now.'

And that was how our pop group started.

I walked back home across the fields, along the high white road, light-headed with the idea. The telephone was ringing as I opened the front door. It was the American agent to tell me that the last lot of tenants had refused to pay their rent because there was no dishwasher, no tumble dryer, no microwave in my quaint and atmospheric home. 'Well, you're just going to have to make the money up yourself, aren't you?' I told him and rang off. I glared at the house which gazed back mournfully at me. 'You listen to me,' I said to it, 'it's no use you sitting there feeling sorry for yourself and trying to make me feel guilty. You don't scare me any more. If you start playing up and leaking and peeling and crumbling, I'll sell you and push off round the world. So just you watch it and pull yourself together. I haven't got time for you and your blockages. I'm going to be a pop group.'

Three days later, Harriet and Jane came home to supper and Sophie came back from Cornwall. We sat round the kitchen table like a proper family again, eating Pot Noodles and drinking Co-op wine, laughing at the memories of the market stall and the puppet show and the terrible Battle of the Mini-Skirt.

After three glasses of wine, I was drunk enough to recite 'The Song of the Good Woman' to my daughters.

Jane was amazed and impressed. 'I always knew you had it in you,' she said.

Harriet was practical. 'What are you going to do with it?' she asked.

But Sophie was deeply shocked and offended that such thoughts and words could ever cross the mind and lips of her mother. 'It isn't . . . suitable,' she said.

'Suitable for what, for heaven's sake?' asked Jane impatiently.

'For mothers,' replied Sophie crossly. 'Mothers don't write things like that.'

'Like what?' asked Jane.

'About their thighs,' said Sophie primly. 'And anyway, you never did run the Brownie Pack. You weren't organised enough.'

'What are you going to do with it?' asked Harriet again. I drank another glass of wine and played for time by reciting 'The Song of the Sink' to them.

> That's why some of us go crazy
> And others take to drink,
> And some of us screw . . .

I stopped.

'Go on,' said Harriet.

'I've forgotten the next line,' I said feebly.

> And some of us screw
> The seat to the loo,

said Sophie and roared with laughter at her own wit.

'Yes, that'll do,' I said.

> Or take up pen and ink.
> We need a bit of glamour, bit of sparkle, bit of
>   glitter,
> Bit of something-round-the-corner when we're
>   sitting in the litter . . .

Sophie guffawed loudly and vulgarly. 'That's pathetic,' she said.

'Why?' I was getting cross.

'Well, I just get this picture of you sitting in the cat litter tray waiting for something exciting to happen. It's ridiculous.'

'Oh shut up, Sophie,' said Jane and then she and Harriet began to giggle helplessly at the idea of their mother sitting in the cat litter.

'And Pavarotti skips into the kitchen, goes down on one knee and sings you a passionate aria,' gasped Harriet.

They all three rolled on the floor, speechless with laughter.

Then Harriet sat up and asked her question again. 'But what are you going to do with them?'

I looked at them with cool dignity. 'Susie, Jean and I are going to form a pop group.'

Sophie stopped laughing and stared at me in horror. 'But you are my mother,' she protested. 'Mothers can't possibly be in pop groups. Don't you realise that my friends' mothers are doctors and teachers and on the PTA? Some of them are even grandmothers. Why can't you be normal?' She stormed out of the room and thundered up the stairs.

'Ignore her, Mum,' said Harriet. 'She's just being pubic. Jane and me'll calm her down.'

'Jane and I,' I said automatically, as Harriet followed Sophie up the stairs.

Chapter 36

The next morning, as I was hauling an ugly tangle of tights out of the washing machine, Jane said, 'What are you going to do about the music?'

'What music?'

'Music. You know, for your pop group. It's all very well to write amazing words, but somebody's got to write the tunes and play the music, haven't they?'

I hadn't even thought about it until then. 'It's just,' went on Jane, 'that Chas is a brilliant pianist and composer. He might be interested. He's back with his parents on the Riverside Road. His father's a brigadier or something. I can put you in touch if you like.' She borrowed two pounds for her bus fare and went off to her vegetables.

I thought about what she had said. Of course we needed a composer. Susie's guitar talents didn't go far beyond 'Yellow Bird' and 'Sloop John B.' What we needed was someone with pizzazz and oomph and sparkle.

I met the others in Shangri-la and told them what Jane had said about Chas.

'He sounds a bit good for us,' said Susie, but Jean remembered baby-sitting for him eighteen years before, which made him seem a lot less daunting and so we agreed that Jane could mention us to him. When I thought about it, I realized she was paying me an enormous compliment. That evening she rang Chas up and invited him to meet us.

He wore black leather and a pigtail and earrings, but when you got through that, his eyes were gentle and his smile was kind. He showed no surprise or distaste at being confronted by three middle-aged women who wanted to form a pop group and he invited us to his parents' house the next morning, which was a Saturday, so that we could hear him play the piano and decide whether or not he was what he wanted.

We went to the house and Chas' father opened the door. To my horror I recognised him as *The* Brigadier, the one who had led the campaign against the Bible. Fortunately he did not recognise me and he had obviously never heard of our pop group, but he seemed wearily resigned to his son's strange visitors. Chas appeared and led us into the music room.

Jean, Susie and I sat in a row along the Chesterfield and Chas began to play. As soon as his fingers touched the keys, we knew that we were in the presence of something extraordinary and that Jane had not exaggerated when she told us he was brilliant. Chas could take you from a 1920s tea dance to a symphony orchestra to a heavy rock session within minutes.

'He's too good for us,' whispered Susie.

'No, he's not,' said Jean firmly, 'we're good too. Remember Wet Breaks in 4A.'

There was a break in the music and we applauded. 'I don't know what sort of thing you're looking for.' Chas was modest. I handed him 'The Song of the Good Woman' and as he read it a slow, delighted smile grew across his face until he was laughing out loud. 'Give me a day to play around with it and I'll ring you when I've come up with some ideas.'

Early the next morning, Sunday, Chas rang and said he'd got an idea for a tune for 'The Song of the Good Woman', and would we all like to go round and listen to it after he'd played the organ for matins. At half past eleven, Susie, Jean, Sophie and I gathered round the piano and Chas began to play. Once again I shivered at his talent. The rhythm was strong and punchy and the tune was exciting and unpredictable. But we picked it up and before long we were belting the song out through the open windows and into the surprised ears of the Sunday morning strollers on the Riverside Road.

'Give it some oomph,' said Chas. 'Imagine the man you most desire is standing at the end of the road. Turn your energy on to him. Make him look at you and listen to you and want you.' I was a little taken aback to hear a young man of twenty speaking to over a hundred and thirty years' worth of womanhood like that, but I tried to do as I was told. I couldn't think of anybody real so I made somebody up. I was dying to know who the others were lusting after but had the delicacy not to ask.

So now we had a song and a tune and a pianist. What next? 'We need a gig,' said Chas. I visualised some sort of horse-drawn cart out of Oklahoma and wondered why we needed one.

'What we should do,' Jean was being practical again, 'is advertise ourselves in the Post Office window and the Parish Magazine and then people will book us for concerts.'

'Gigs,' said Chas. Then he pointed out that one song, no matter how brilliant, was not going to be enough to launch us on a glittering career. So I gave him the others I had written and he took them away and wrote tunes for them all.

We sat down to compose an advertisement for the Post Office window and the Parish Magazine. That was when we realised that we hadn't got a name. Hours went by while we ground our brains in the kitchen trying to think of something sparkling. 'Menopop' seemed quite a good generic title and someone came up with 'Mid-Life Crisis' which was the nearest thing to all right but which somehow lacked pizzazz.

Then Harriet walked in to make herself a peanut butter sandwich. 'What on earth's the matter with you lot?' she asked.

'We can't think of a name for the group,' Susie said despondently.

'It's obvious,' said Harriet through a mouthful of peanut butter. 'It sticks out a mile.' She grinned and winked at Chas. 'It's "Hot Flush and the Toy Boy" of course.'

Of course. It was obvious. It couldn't be anything else. We composed the advertisement:

> 'Hot Flush and the Toy Boy'
> Britain's only menopausal pop group.
> Available for gigs and private parties.

We put it into the Post Office window for a fortnight at twenty pence a week and waited for the world to discover us.

Nothing happened for ten days and then the President of the WI rang up to say that she was organising a charity concert in the Village Hall and would Hot Flush be part of it?

Chapter 37

It was the night of the charity concert. Hot Flush and the
Toy Boy was due to appear on the stage of the Village Hall
between the Myrtle Fanshawe School of Dance and the
church choir, and it was terrified. I looked in the dressing
room mirror and saw the multi-coloured tights I'd pinched
from Harriet hugging my legs and four-inch stiletto heels
turning me into a tart. Susie was zipped into a black leather
mini-skirt, black tights, bright yellow ankle socks, stilettos
and an Afro wig, and Jean was awe-inspiring in an off-the-
shoulder string vest, lycra shorts, half-inch false eyelashes
behind her glasses and DMs. We all jangled with jewels,
especially Chas, who wore Bermuda shorts, vest and
sunglasses.

Five minutes before we were on, Jean gasped, 'My
eyelashes've got stuck to my glasses. I can't blink.' Her eyes
were stuck wide open, which must be like having agora-
phobia and claustrophobia at the same time.

My terror turned to hysteria and Susie whimpered, 'I
think I'm going to be sick.'

Then Jean wrenched her glasses off and the eyelashes
came off with them and we heard the compère say:

'And now, we come to a historic moment in the annals of
entertainment. For the first time on the British Stage, we
present an entirely new phenomenon in the pop world.
Ladies and Gentlemen: Hot Flush and the Toy Boy.'

The stage curtains of the village hall jerked back and we stood there in the limelight before our dumbstruck audience. Straight away the terror vanished and Susie, Jean and I were wild, glitzy women, flashing our eyes and gyrating our bodies at the astounded village. I remembered what Chas had said about directing the oomph to an object of desire at the back of the hall, so I oomphed and slid my eyes sideways and knew that the others had remembered it too. Terrifying messages flowed from Susie's leather-clutched thighs, and Jean's DMs beat a ferocious rhythm on to the floor of the stage.

The audience began to whistle; Chas struck up the opening bars and we were off.

> I'm going to be a beauty queen
> I'm going to be a star.

We leaned diagonally on to our ecstatic audience, rotating our hips and shoulders and beaming our lime-lighted lust to the back of the hall . . .

> I'm only froth and bubbles
> I'm just here for the lust

Roars of delighted laughter greeted the offer. We finished the song and the audience burst into cheers and catcalls and cries for more, so we sang it again and flounced off the stage to riotous applause. We knew what it was to be a success.

What we did not know, however, was that there was a Contact in the audience, a young man with a recording studio who was married to the president of the WI's son-in-law's sister. He had been cajoled against his better judgement into coming to the concert and had slid surreptitiously into the back row of the hall when the houselights went down. From there, sitting next to Dick the Relationship, he had received the full impact of Jean's eyes, Susie's thighs and my lycra legs.

'There's somebody here who wants to meet you,' said the President of the WI in the interval and she pointed her son-in-law's sister's husband at us.

He smiled and shook our hands and introduced himself as Oliver Ockerton, then he handed me a card which said, 'Ockerton's Echoes. Rehearsal and Recording Studio. Promotional Service, Multi-Track Mix, Professional Advice.' 'I liked your song,' said Oliver Ockerton, 'and I've come to offer you a free demo tape recording.'

'Gosh,' I said, not at all sure what a demo tape recording was, but realising it was a good thing to be offered one.

'What I mean is,' continued Oliver Ockerton, 'that I believe your group has got potential. It's a completely original idea; no one else has thought of Menopop. I want you all to come to my studio so that I can record you. Free of charge.'

We flew high on excitement and floated home through the darkened street, past the Co-op and the Post Office, knowing that we were no longer prisoners of the Family Allowance and cat food. We were a pop group on the road to success.

Chapter 38

Three days later, Hot Flush and the Toy Boy drove up to the Ockerton Echoes Recording Studio (which was actually a prefab on an industrial estate) in the Jenkins' Landrover. There was another group already playing in the rehearsal room, bashing out a wild song about lost love and retribution. When it had wailed its final lament, it put down its instruments and came to talk to us. Beneath ear-ringed noses, the mouths which had howled out the song smiled and introduced their owners as Oz (part-time window cleaner and guitarist), Fizz (part-time chef and drummer), and Moses (part-time gardener and vocalist/ songwriter). 'They're called "Osmosis",' said Oliver.

We followed him into the studio where drums and keyboards and cables and speakers lay in tangled profusion. 'Carry on with the jam,' said Oliver to Osmosis, and Oz picked up an electric guitar and plucked out a tune. The rhythm was taken up by Fizz and Moses began to hum the melody. I wondered where the jam was.

And then it was our turn. Chas sat down at the piano and warmed up with the opening bars of 'Good Woman' while we hummed along to loosen up our tonsils. Oliver Ockerton's assistant flitted around us, fixing microphones, plugging things in and unplugging them again while Oliver fiddled about with a lot of keys and levers and headphones.

We, Hot Flush, stood in front of a row of microphones.

'Whenever you're ready,' said Oliver. Chas rang out the opening bar, I took a deep breath and we launched into the song. We went right through it and then Oliver played it back to us. It sounded terrible.

'Don't worry. Ignore everything except the last thirty seconds,' Oliver said. 'I was playing about with balance till then.' And sure enough, the last verse came across, loud and clear and challenging.

> So look out, World, I'm coming.
> Hey look out world, it's me.
> I'll set your pulses drumming,
> And I'm only forty-three.

'OK,' said Oliver. 'Now we'll do it again.' And we did it again. And again and again and again until we'd got it right and it was half past two and time to flee the world of showbiz and rush home to meet our children from school.

And there, waiting for us, was the other, warm, lovely cosy world of dinner money, school photographs, tea, homework and ordinariness. As Sophie galloped across the playground to meet me, that world felt very safe and comforting. She and I walked hand in hand, stopping to buy buns for a treat, talking to the other mothers, greeting familiar dogs and babies. Ockerton's Echoes with its microphones, demo tapes and gigs and jam belonged on a different planet.

Chapter 39

But that other planet called to us until we found ourselves turning into a local success, into a group that gigged for expenses in pubs and at parties, a group with a name that people in Tarminster and district knew.

We were booked to perform one night at the Tarminster Arts Centre, which was a converted warehouse with a lot of abstract sculptures and meaningful photographs in its foyer, where middle-aged teachers mingled nostalgically with rock bands and artists, drinking white wine and talking of Art and the Meaning of Life and Poverty.

We were there to support the support band, which was an all-girls' group called Convolvulus Villa. The main attraction was Sweetness and Light and it looked very dangerous as it rattled its drumsticks and did suggestive things with its guitars. It consisted of four massively broad and hairy men with tattoos and waist-length locks who scowled and swore and swigged beer out of bottles. One of them caught my eye and blushed and I realised he had been at playgroup with Jane. I looked more closely at the others who smiled sheepishly and looked away and I realised that behind the hair and denim were three little boys from Harriet's year in primary school. The drummer raised his sticks. 'One-two-one-two,' said a technician and the drummer crashed his sticks on to the drums. My mind shot back to the day when he had cried and his mother had had to come and collect him because he didn't want to be in the school nativity play.

The technician twiddled his knobs and slid his levers up and down the sound board, the drummer drummed and the walls and floor of the Arts Centre began to vibrate. My ears and brain went numb, undiscovered pulses in my head, chest and throat began to pulsate with the drums and I thought I'd have a stroke. I went out into the corridor where Convolvulus Villa was bouncing about orgasmically, rolling on the floor and grasping its legs. 'They're politically lesbian,' explained Jean in a whisper.

Convolvulus Villa stopped bouncing and came up to talk. They were sweet and very kind and they went to find cups of tea for us. 'It's a bit loud if you're not used to it,' they said. There was a pause in the sound testing and we ventured back into the auditorium. Fans of Sweetness and Light lay around the floor in black jeans and waistcoats, surrounded by wires, drinking from bottles, proud to be part of the in-crowd. Scattered among them in solid, respectable blocks, sitting upright on chairs, staring straight ahead of them, clutching their handbags and keeping their coats on, were little groups of middle-aged and elderly women. I saw Nola Gleeson and the Vicar's wife, the President of the WI and the Water Bailiff's wife, the Traffic Warden and the wise and woolly virgins from the church and I wondered what on earth they were all doing there.

As we climbed the steps on to the stage for our performance I could feel the excitement begin to run through me. The lights were harsh in my eyes as Chas began to play and all I could see in the auditorium now was a blur of faces and bodies. 'I'll show you lot,' I thought. 'I'll make you sit up and take notice.' I threw back my head and smiled sideways like the Mona Lisa at my imaginary hero.

Look at me, Mister, I've got the best legs in this place tonight.

'Give it some oomph,' whispered Chas' voice in my head and I oomphed towards my hero, wooing him to want me.

'So look out, World, I'm coming,' called Susie, Jean and I as we dared our audience to join in the last verse. A great chorus of voices soared and sang it with us and as the lights went down the women rose and shrieked for us to sing the song again.

Hot and flushed with success, we left the stage and went to the back of the theatre to watch the rest of the show.

Convolvulus Villa bounced on, dressed in woad and Victorian evening gowns, plucking electric guitars and singing cross songs about schizophrenia and sex. But I could never quite make out the words or really hear the notes. One of them pretended to stab another with a retractable toy dagger and a blood capsule burst all over the victim's bodice. It was very confusing and alarming. They raged and bled and bounced for nearly an hour, and then it was time for Sweetness and Light.

Once again the music exploded and filled me up. I glanced towards the door at the back of the auditorium to make sure that I had a clear pathway to escape, and a huge bouncer caught my eye and jerked his head in the direction of the corridor. I followed him.

'Have a pair of ear-plugs. Terrible, isn't it? They'll all be brain damaged by the time they're twenty-five. I prefer Bach myself.'

Ear-plugged, I went back into the auditorium. The lead singer of Sweetness and Light was screaming into his microphone, doing things with his pelvis that made Elvis look like Fonteyn. I would have been shocked, but I remembered escorting him to the school lavatory when I was a Mother Helper in the reception class and he was a Rising Five. He rushed offstage and then swung on again wearing a jockstrap, high heels and a curly black wig. His fans grew frantic. They writhed and screamed and reached out to touch him. I caught his eye by accident again and he blushed again. Was he too remembering how hard he and I had struggled with Peter and Jane and their wretched dog and its wretched ball all those years ago?

The lights went down on Sweetness and Light. Their fans screamed and wept and writhed dutifully and then the screams began to change into a new and rhythmic chant. 'Hot Flush, Hot Flush, Hot Flush,' it pounded as the mothers and grandmothers, virgins, vicars' wives and traffic wardens of Honeyford and Tarminster rose up and stamped and clapped and begged for us to sing their song again.

It was most irregular. Support bands go on first. Support bands are supposed to know their place, to keep to their proper stations in life. But Sweetness and Light and Convolvulus Villa had generous natures. 'Go on,' they said, 'it's you they want, it's you they're calling for.'

We climbed back on the stage again, Chas began to play and we began to sing. They kept the house lights on this time and I could see the women singing with us. I looked across their heads to where my hero would have been standing. If he had existed. And there, right at the back of the auditorium, clapping and shouting and stamping and laughing with delight and pride in me, were all my daughters.

Chapter 40

The phone rang and Oliver Ockerton said, 'Listen to me. It's time to make a record.'

'What?'

'I mean it,' said Oliver. 'You were brilliant last night. They loved you. It's time to make a single and go for the Big Time. It's all a question of timing and I know the mood is right.'

I sat alone in Shangri-la and wondered what was going to happen. I was safe where I was, doing the songs for fun, as a joke, as a batty housewife with my feet on the ground, in the mud, on the pavement. Did I want the Big Time?

Did I want the Big Time? Of course I did. You bet your life I did. I wanted it and I deserved it and at last it was within my reach. I had done my best to be a mother. I had washed floors and de-loused heads, I had helped with homework, mopped up tears, mended broken hearts. And I had come a long way since then. Now I could make a sausage, catch a fish, row a boat, clean a house, drive a bus, deliver a calf. I could write a song as well and now the time had come to sing it as loudly as I could.

And there didn't have to be a choice. Jane had said it all those years ago when we had struggled with her maths and I had glued God's head back into place. 'You mustn't give up now,' she'd said. 'You'll let us all down if you give up now.' So it wouldn't be Home and Family versus Hot Flush and the Toy Boy. I could have them both. And I would.

I went to find Jean and Susie and told them what Oliver Ockerton had said.

As usual, Jean spoke for us all. 'If we don't give it a go, we'll never know what it might have been like and we'll go to our graves wondering.'

'In any case,' said Susie, 'I don't expect anyone'll notice.'

But Oliver Ockerton was right. 'The Song of the Good Woman' touched something in the hearts and wombs of Britain as a company of pluggers called Socket and Sparrow took up our record and cajoled local radio stations all over the country into playing it. A huge subterranean wave of women surged to the surface and flowed inexorably along the High Streets and into the record shops to buy our song.

On the Sunday of the week in which we broke through to the menopausal awareness of the nation, Sophie and Charley came screaming into the living room. 'You're a New Entry,' they gasped. 'You're Number Thirty-Eight in the Top Forty. They've just read you out on Pick of the Pops.' We tuned into Radio One and I felt a flush of excitement as our song filled the house.

Oliver was on the phone as soon as the record was over. 'We've got to move fast. We've got to tell "Top of the Pops" you're available for recording on Wednesday week.'

'Hang on,' I said, 'I'll have to check it's all right with the others.' Jean said it was all right with her as long as nobody wanted to have a funeral on Wednesday week and Susie said it was all right with her as long as Mike could arrange to borrow another Landrover because Wednesday was Tarminster market day. I would have to change Sophie's brace-tightening appointment at the dentist, but otherwise, Wednesday week was clear.

Oliver arrived to explain how things worked. This was

Sunday. All week, Ken Socket of Socket and Sparrow would plug the record to make sure the record stations kept on playing it, and then on Friday morning, Tim Sparrow would go to the office of the 'Top of the Pops' producer and tell him that Hot Flush and the Toy Boy was available to appear on his programme next week.

'I'll bet he'll be pleased,' said Jean.

'It doesn't work like that,' said Oliver. 'All the pluggers will be there trying to make him take their stuff. Tim's got to persuade him that he wants you more than he wants the others. And he'll only consider 'Good Woman' if she's still going up in the charts by next Sunday. If she's going down, forget it.'

We sat in Shangri-la and discussed our set. We decided that a background of kitchen sink, draining board and drying underwear would be fitting, especially if the draining board could turn into Chas' keyboard when the moment was ripe. And as long as we hadn't gone down in the charts, we would drive the whole caboodle up the M5 to the television studios on the Wednesday morning in the Jenkins' Landrover.

Early on Friday morning, Tim Sparrow went to plug us to the 'Top of the Pops' boss. He rang us at midday to say that things looked very hopeful but you couldn't be sure of anything till the Monday morning when the boss made his final decision. But the omens were auspicious as long as we didn't go down in the charts.

We didn't. On the Sunday we listened to 'Pick of the Pops' ('I haven't done this since I was twenty,' said Susie) and heard ourselves listed at twenty-five. Jean and Susie and I were drunk with excitement, but Mike and Kevin took refuge in Shangri-la with cans of beer and cheese sandwiches to escape from the talk of sets and runs and DATs and pluggers. ('What the hell is a DAT anyway?' Mike asked. 'It's a small tape of our instrumental backing of course,' said Susie. 'Of course it is,' said Kevin. 'Fancy you not knowing that.')

We found an old kitchen sink and draining board in a Jenkins outhouse. Dirty crockery and dangling underwear had never been a problem for me.

Chapter 41

On the crucial Monday morning, Tim Sparrow had to present himself at the 'Top of the Pops' office to get the final go-ahead. It was only a formality now. We were all waiting in Oliver Ockerton's office for the phone to ring. 'Here we go,' said Oliver.

'Oh,' said Oliver Ockerton and put the phone down. We knew at once that everything was off. 'He only takes eight bands,' said Oliver Ockerton. 'You were the ninth.'

We trailed back home, I took Mistake and caught the ferry across to the other side of the river. 'Oh well,' I thought. 'It's probably better to be peaceful and safe.'

On Tuesday, I washed up all the dirty crockery I'd been saving for our set and ironed all the dangling underwear.

On Wednesday, Mike went off to Tarminster Market to sell some sheep, Kevin went off to carve a rood screen and Jean, Susie and I sat at home and told each other how glad we were to be peaceful and safe and contented.

At five past eleven the telephone rang. 'Can you get the girls together?' said Oliver Ockerton urgently. 'I've just had a phone call from "Top of the Pops". One of the bands can't go on because the producer says he won't record them unless they stop being explicit with their guitars and they say they won't so they've gone and he wants you instead.'

We loaded the kitchen sink, the clean crockery and a load of wet laundry into the Landrover, bundled our costumes into carrier bags, grabbed our available children, left notes for the others and headed off along the motorway. Two hours later we drove up to the gates of the television studios past a queue of bedraggled maidens who were sitting patiently on the pavement in the lunchtime rain. They were not waiting to see us, explained the security man who opened the gates to let us in, shooing the maidens away as they drifted towards him. Lorenzo Stacey was recording today and the maidens had been waiting devotedly for a glimpse of their god since half past nine that morning. I saw Sophie turn pale at the name of Lorenzo Stacey. Our personal Minder arrived to meet us, our set and props were unloaded from the Landrover and we followed the Minder into the studio.

Assistant floor managers glided quickly and expertly between huge mobile cameras that swooped and plunged and reversed at speed, ridden by disdainful cameramen wearing headphones who had no time to worry about slow movers on the studio floor. 'They're only rehearsing,' said the Minder. 'They work out their moves without actually recording so that they know exactly what to do when it's the real thing.'

There were four stages arranged in a circle around the studio. On the one closest to us, a bouncy group was singing a cheerful Gospel song to a bongo drum. 'Who are they?' I whispered to Sophie.

'Snap, Crackle and Pop, of course,' she whispered back.

Jean looked at me with scorn. 'Even I knew that.' We had to duck and retreat as a camera zoomed noiselessly and suddenly backwards at us.

'He'll need to work out your sound levels,' explained the Minder as Snap, Crackle and Pop sang its final hallelujah and the Floor Manager ushered us on to the second stage. The producer waved a signal from his control box, our DAT began to play, Chas mimed the keyboard/draining board and we sang 'The Song of the Good Woman' until our sound levels were right and the camera shots were fixed.

Lorenzo Stacey sauntered across the studio floor. You could feel his cool sexiness ten feet away. We watched, entranced and shivering, as he breathed into his microphone. He was like some sleek race-horse, pent-up and reined in at the starting line, beautiful and gleaming, saving his real energy for the moment when it would be needed. This was not the moment.

A woman called Jennifer stood on the third stage and sang a warning song about the dangers of a new love and we went off to make-up.

An hour later we were back in the studio, dressed and ready for the first run-through. 'You needn't sing this one if you want to save your voices,' the Floor Manager explained. 'It's up to you. Some people like to use it as a warm-up, some like to save their energy.' We looked at each other. 'Let's just mime and hum,' said Susie.

We were scheduled to go on fifth, between Lorenzo Stacey and Snap, Crackle and Pop. We stood shoulder to shoulder with the stars, watching each other on this first complete run-through as the presenter rattled his patter into the microphone. I found a space on some steps leading up to one of the stages and sat down on it, next to a comfortable woman who was knitting something stripy on four needles. Jennifer was socking out her warning from the other side of the studio and the comfortable woman knitted in time to her beat. She smiled at me. 'You've met my son?' she asked, leaning plumply backwards. Lorenzo Stacey sat on her far side staring moodily across the studio space. 'I'm knitting him some socks.' I stole another look at Lorenzo's profile and tried to imagine him in stripy four-ply socks.

The lights went down on Jennifer and came up on the

second stage. Lorenzo rose to his feet in a single, graceful, uncurling movement and sprang on to the stage. Again he seemed to me to be a beautiful and highly strung animal, holding himself and his energies in check until it was time to let everything go.

The audience had arrived, it was time for the real thing, and the place was alive with suspended excitement. Circles of light whirled and spun and flickered high above our heads, the cameras raced silently and unpredictably around the floor, the presenter set the mood and the pace and the show began: Ring Road, Cantata, Jennifer, Lorenzo Stacey.

He came to life electrically in front of his worshippers. He caressed them with his voice, wooed them with his body and spurned them with his eyes and they wept and reached out for him while all the time his mother knitted on.

Lorenzo's song was over, his lights went down and ours came up. We faced upstage, wrapped in the flowered overalls, backs to the audience, facing the sink and the draining board and the piles of crockery and washing. Chas popped up from behind the draining board like a jack-in-a-box and played our opening bars. His words still whispered in my head: 'Think of the man you most desire in all the world and direct your oomph at him.'

I turned around, undid the flowered overall and strode forward to the edge of the stage, rocking and swaying and laughing in lycra and high heels. A sweeping beam of light caught the faces of the audience for a second and there was a glimpse of Sophie cheering us on and Lorenzo Stacey's mother waving her knitting needles in time to our rhythm. As the lights exploded like fireworks around us and the cameras bowed and reared and bowed again before us and the beat of our song filled the studio, I knew that we were flying at last, that the sparklers of 4A had done what they were meant to do. The high white road shone in the studio

lights, it swooped on and on and over the hills and far away
and I could follow it as far as it wanted to go.

> So look out, World, I'm coming,
> Hey look out, World, it's me.
> I'll set your pulses drumming,
> And I'm only forty-three.

Anything could happen.